About Jon Whale, PhD

Jon Whale is an independent research scientist working exclusively on medical applications. He is also a psychologist, graphologist, electronic design and development engineer, and an organic chemist. Currently he is engaged in designing and manufacturing electronic Energy Medicine instruments for doctors and other medical professionals. Some of his former projects included the design and development of X-ray image intensifiers, lasers, medical scanners, nerve-pulse stimulus and biofeedback instruments. Jon Whale lives in England where he continues his research and design work in Electronic Energy Medicine.

THE CATALYST
OF POWER

Jon Whale, Ph.D.

FINDHORN
Press

First published by Findhorn Press in 2001

ISBN 1-899171-73-8

British Library Cataloguing-in-Publication Data.
A catalogue record for this book is available from the British Library.

Library of Congress Catalog Card Number: 00-109625

Script, drawings, photographs and artwork © 2001 by Jon Whale
Editorial director Dr. Angela Blaen
Publishing Editor Carol Shaw
Layout by Jon Whale and Thierry Bogliolo
Front cover design by Dale Vermeer
Back cover design by Thierry Bogliolo

Printed and bound in Finland

Published by
Findhorn Press

The Park, Findhorn   P.O. Box 13939
Forres IV36 3TY   Tallahassee
Scotland   Florida 32317-3939, USA
Tel 01309 690582   Tel 850 893 2920
Fax 01309 690036   Fax 850 893 3442

e-mail info@findhornpress.com
findhornpress.com

Contents

Table of Illustrations

chapter 1

chapter 2

chapter 3

chapter 4

chapter 5

chapter 6

chapter 7

appendix I

appendix II

appendix III

appendix V

appendix VI

Acknowledgments

I wish to express my thanks to the thousands of individuals who have contributed and participated over the years. I would especially like to convey my indebtedness to those patients whose illness and suffering provided the testing ground for the medical discoveries outlined in this book. I hope that my rather arbitrary choice of accounts of personal experiences express the immense possibilities of these discoveries adequately enough to spur the curiosity of fellow researchers and practitioners.

Disclaimer

This book is a reference work, not intended to diagnose, prescribe or treat. The information contained herein is in no way to be considered as a substitute for consultation with a professional physician. Those who use the Assemblage Point techniques described in this book do so by their own choice and, while if done according to the instructions in this book they may prove efficacious, neither the author nor the publisher promise, guarantee or accept responsibility for any specific results.

Editorial Preface

Dr. Angela Blaen, BA, PhD
Research Fellow
University of Exeter, Devon, England

Today, 19 August 2000, I became the first person in the world to have the existence of their Assemblage Point independently scientifically proved and its energy recorded. This was the thrilling culmination of a year's work on this book with its author, Jon Whale. During this year I have had several Assemblage Point shifts and can confirm their profoundly beneficial physical and psychological results. In addition, I have had my severe long-term asthma cured by electronic gem lamp therapy. Few editors can support the contents of a book so enthusiastically!

The Catalyst of Power is an extraordinary and unique book. It not only takes the form of a challenge to conventional medical practices but also gives each individual the opportunity to be in control of their own physical and psychological health. This book marks a new beginning and stands out in sharp contrast to all the alternative or complementary works on health written over the last century, because of its sound basis in both modern science and traditional learning. Above all, it is a book full of timely optimism.

Long awaited in certain circles, this outline of Dr. Whale's work demonstrates his unquestionable position both as the current expert on the human Assemblage Point and as a ground breaking pioneer in energy medicine in the form of electronic gem lamp therapy. His combination of diagnosis and treatment of the human energy field via its crucial Assemblage Point plus his knowledge and skill in treating physical and psychological disease with gem lamp therapy is powerful, supremely practical and has compelling results. My own research into contemporary and traditional healing, lapidaries and the use of gems enables me to give due respect to Jon Whale's work and its conclusions.

Although deeply scientific, this is also a work of passion, compassion and concern for humanity. Inevitably it is also at times angry. The author's frustration in the face of some contemporary medical failures is all too obvious. Any pioneer for change shares similar moments of frustration along with the determination to improve whatever situation he finds. Jon Whale's highly individual, independent research and clinical experience of many years reveals a tenacity and an intellectual freedom rarely found within an institution or corporate body. If such work is typical of the new millennium, mankind's future can be greatly enhanced.

Introduction

It is rare that a researcher has an opportunity to present an original contribution containing numerous major scientific and medical discoveries, based on some 30 years of research. The discoveries and techniques outlined here are so universally important for humanity, that I predict that this book will be of interest to a wide body of readers for a very long time to come. It is much more than a scientific or medical book for it contains powerful knowledge, together with the precise details of the techniques for the application of this knowledge for the benefit of humanity. Knowledge is power and the discovery of the human Assemblage Point and its total domination over our birth, development, mental and physical health and our death will eventually be acknowledged as one of the great scientific discoveries of the last century.

The non-scientific reader will not find this book tough going. I have written this book specifically for a non-scientific audience. The knowledge and techniques are so powerful and effective that I felt they should be freely available to everyone. I have concluded that, no matter what their training or background, those who have read my earlier papers or have experienced the dramatic beneficial effects of Assemblage Point management, have gained very definite and long lasting new awareness, together with profound improvements in their mental and physical health and spiritual well being accompanied with an enrichment in their relationships and standards of living.

The information which is presented here is not theoretical, it has been tried and tested over many years on thousands of ordinary men and women. For patients with chronic health problems, it has provided a short cut back to health, normality and freedom. Many readers have personally undertaken to learn and put into practice the methods outlined here and have been able to put the knowledge into practical application in their own lives. Many of them can now provide profound assistance to other people burdened with chronic mental or physical health problems. They can testify and confirm the effectiveness of the methods.

At first glance this may look like a medical book, this is because it has been necessary to use the application of the information not just for the benefits of ordinary people but also to inform the medical profession. The results had to be proved and the only way to do that was to test them out on difficult problems. It was not a deliberate decision to set about this work, it came about spontaneously, because so many patients turned up presenting with conditions requiring a solution. The methods have been used to treat and cure patients with psychological and physical diseases, which have not responded to orthodox or alternative complementary medicine. This work over the years has provided thousands of patients' case studies, some of which I have included to prove to you the efficacy and benefits of the discovery of the human Assemblage Point. I have included sufficient examples of people's personal experiences to enable most readers to find that they or someone close to them will be able to relate in a meaningful way to at least one of them.

This book and the methods and techniques expressed here have slowly developed over a long period. There has been more than adequate time to develop, improve and prove the methods used, under adequately controlled conditions. There has been sufficient time to integrate all of the years of collected data to furnish a current scientific and medical position with which the author is relatively satisfied.

All forms of power have to be contained and controlled with sobriety and good ethics. Where any form of power is concerned, safety rules and standards of use have to be applied and I have set out here a working base of guidelines and standards which should be adhered to or improved upon.

Over the last ten years or so, many others, including researchers, doctors and therapists, have independently experienced and confirmed what is documented in this book. Other people, from differing backgrounds and having other expertise and goals, can now utilise these methods in pursuit of their personal growth, professional development and areas of research. Those interested in using Assemblage Point science within their fields of interest now have numerous thoroughly tested methods and techniques to apply. I am confident that the publication of the Assemblage Point papers will trigger a new enthusiastic wave of scientific and medical research, which will bring enormous benefits to the planet.

This book exposes and solves many mysteries of antiquity. The Assemblage Point is the missing link which has been holding back scientific, medical and social progress. Indeed history has wasted colossal sums of money and human effort because conventional science has overlooked the human Assemblage Point and many millions of humans have suffered and are continuing to suffer unnecessarily.

This view is to a large extent endorsed by The Oxford Textbook of Medicine. It summarises the evolution of contemporary western medicine as follows, So far as world health is concerned, there have been only two areas of significant medical advancement in the last one hundred and fifty years. In the first half of the eighteenth century infectious diseases such as cholera, smallpox, typhoid and tuberculosis were some of the names that triggered panic and terror. With the understanding of the germ theory, vaccination, improved sanitation and the introduction of sterile procedures in hospitals, by the turn of the century, infectious diseases had largely been controlled. Leading up to 1960, the discovery and development of antibiotics and other selective killing agents that destroyed bacterial infections, but not the patient, formed the second medical breakthrough. In the last forty years there has been no similarly significant medical breakthrough that has improved world health.

Virtually no advances have been made to cure diseases such as psoriasis, eczema, asthma, various allergies, irritable bowel syndrome, Parkinson's disease, strokes, kidney failure, diabetes, myalgic encephalomyelitis (M.E.), arthritis, rheumatism, thrombosis, multiple sclerosis (M.S.), viral infections, varicose ulcers, sterility and so on. Orthodox medicine can only prescribe medication and therapies to comfort and support the patient. Neither has the alternative and complementary medicine sector any worthwhile solutions for these conditions. There are millions of patients suffering with these diseases and the cost in manpower and taxes runs into billions of pounds each year.

Even after one hundred years of psychotherapy, the mental health situation is not any better. In the United Kingdom mental health problems alone are responsible for over 90 million lost working days each year. Orthodox medicine is no closer to finding a cure for schizophrenia, senile dementia, manic depression or even depression. Crime, violence, discrimination, antisocial behaviour, drug addiction, vagrancy and divorce have all increased since the 1960's. This is despite the ever increasing numbers of social workers, charities, counsellors, psychologists, psychiatrists, psychoanalysts, Gestalt therapists, hypnotherapists, and a huge range of alternative and complementary therapists, probation officers and police.

The proof that the public now perceive that something has gone badly wrong with orthodox medicine is supported by the recent boom in alternative and complementary medicine clinics and therapists. Due to this development, medical doctors are looking for ways to improve their credibility. They are now looking for evidence based results. Doctors know that the placebo effect is between thirty and seventy percent. This effectively means that, if one hundred patients are given a placebo medication or therapy, between thirty and seventy of these patients will report an improvement in their symptoms. The placebo phenomena leaves plenty of business opportunities for charlatans, medications, therapies and other bogus products that do absolutely nothing. Medical doctors are very aware of this and it is not surprising that they are hard to convince and require proof. At the end of the day their professional responsibility is their patients' welfare.

Orthodox and much of the alternative and complementary medicine involves the manipulation of health problems using drugs, herbs, vitamins, minerals, nutrients and dietary controls. In other words, chemicals are the tools of today's medicine. The human body is viewed as a chemical universe, fed through the mouth. Consensus belief is that only chemicals can provide a medical solution.

The United Kingdom's National Health Service is continually complaining about its lack of financial resources, and the same is probably true in most other countries. It blames the shortage of money for its problems and the now all too frequent devastating incidences which its patients experience.

Most of the Health Service's problems would be solved if the medicines and therapies that it prescribed actually worked and cured the patient's disease in the first place. As things are, the prescribed drugs and other therapies are not efficient and they induce side effects. The side effects in turn require further expensive medications and therapies which induce more side effects and compound the patient's symptoms and complaints. Oral and injected medications and supplements are a shotgun approach to health problems. Possibly ninety percent of all therapies are systemic. Systemic treatment means that all of the patient's body gets treated or exposed to the effects of the drug, when only a small part of it requires treatment. Systemic medication is not particularly scientific. Take sciatica for example. Often only a section of just a few millimetres of the patient's spinal nerve is inflamed and requiring treatment, yet the patient is prescribed oral pain killing pills combined with an anti-inflammatory drug. The patient does not realise that this usually ineffective medication for sciatica subjects every one of his organs and glands to its effects. He does not question the effects of the drug's pain killing and anti-inflammatory properties on the rest of his body until the side effects occur.

Over twenty percent of all hospital beds are taken up with patients suffering from iatrogenic disease, that is diseases and conditions caused by previous medical treatments.

Apart from surgery, doctors can hardly prescribe a single treatment which actually specifically targets the parts of their patients which are ill. This is one of the reasons why side effects are so prevalent. The best that can be said about the majority of prescribed orthodox medications and therapies is that they are an "illness maintenance programme" and that much of the relief is provided by comforting propaganda or the nursing profession.

This view is substantiated by numerous recent books, including *Dirty Medicine* by Martin. J. Walker, and *Poisonous Prescriptions* by Dr. Lisa Lanymore-Lim. These two books in particular will make every reader think twice before taking another medicinal drug. Anyone who is interested in finding out more about this subject should also refer to *The Medical Mafia* by Dr. Guylaine Lanctot. This book expounds the details of the manipulation of medical ethics and policies by the multi-national drug companies for the purpose of profiteering at the expense of the patient's welfare and the doctors' reputation and peace of mind. Written for the general public, who are avid but ill-informed consumers of drugs, these publications have sent shock waves through the medical profession.

Dr. Guylaine Lanctot refers to the current orthodox treatment of cancers as "The Medical Holocaust". Her view is authenticated by the fact that over twelve thousand women in the United Kingdom die from breast cancer alone each year. This is just the tip of the iceberg. A more recently commissioned survey reported that some 84,000 needless deaths occur each year as a direct result of substandard medical care. Compared to the three and a half thousand deaths, relating to road accidents each year, our National Health Service hospitals are very dangerous. This disgraceful mortality rate is almost as high as that in World War II. The public has developed a healthy mistrust of chemotherapy and radiation therapy for the treatment of cancer. This is not surprising since the success rate of chemotherapy and radiation therapy is significantly less than the lowest placebo levels mentioned above. The United Kingdom has the worst post treatment survival rates in Western Europe for lung cancer, breast cancer, bowel cancer and heart disease. Louise B. Trulls' book entitled *The Cancell Controversy* quotes the following very interesting figures concerning conventional cancer therapies:

Hardin Jones of the University of California, Berkley, stated that in typical cancer patients, those who refused treatment live, on average, twelve and a half years. Whereas those who accept surgery and other treatment live an average of only three years.

And Dr Lana Levi of the University of California wrote, in 1987, that: most cancer patients in this country die of chemotherapy since it does not eliminate breast, colon or lung cancer. Dr Levi considered that as far back as the 1970s it had been known that women with breast cancer were likely to die faster with chemotherapy than without it.

Dr. Guylaine Lanctot's fortitude and heroism in exposing the current medical practices proliferated by the drug companies forms an exemplary model that all medical doctors truly concerned for their patients' welfare should take on board. As she states, "To be realistic, pharmaceutical companies are basically there to make money, they're not there to advance science . . . . They're not going to go looking for trouble".

Also horrifying is the removal of deceased patient's vital organs without seeking permission from the patient's relatives. Recently the United Kingdom's National Health Service has been involved in a national scandal. Doctors at Europe's largest children's hospital, The Alder Hey Hospital in Liverpool, removed more than 2000 hearts and 850 other organs, including the brains, from babies and young children as well as 400 foetuses. The newspaper reports referred to the scandal as barbaric body snatching. The Liverpool coroner likened the activities of the doctors at The Alder Hey Hospital to the grisly activities of the infamous body snatchers Burke and Hare who lived around the same time as Jack the Ripper in the nineteenth century. How can any parent place their children in the hands of orthodox medical doctors with gross unethical activities like this going on inside hospitals? It is grand theft of the worse possible type, the stealing of human organs. Anyone other than doctors caught involved in stealing any commodity on such a large scale would be given a jail sentence. One might ask how many working hours were spent in surgically removing this number of human organs and how many patients scheduled for surgery had their surgery delayed or cancelled as result?

On the alternative and complementary front, in the United Kingdom there are now as many, if not more, registered alternative therapists than there are medical doctors. Despite this fact, the numbers of people suffering the kinds of diseases and social problems already mentioned are all on the increase. The chronic social psychological level of society has continued to declined since the 1960's. The new legions of alternative and complementary therapists, counsellors, psychotherapists and so on, are not making any real impact on hard medical or social conditions. These therapies can really only be classed as supportive therapies.

With the ongoing exposures of the dereliction of contemporary medicine, the informed patient is left in the wretched position of trying to obtain reliable ethical medical treatment. As already indicated above, the current appaling standard of public medical services is now alarmingly dangerous for all patients, especially those who are uninformed and trusting. The chemical view of medicine is a narrow tunnel reality that has lost sight of the patient and science. Medicine needs a new way of looking at the human body, and the patient, if it is to find solutions to the above diseases and regain the success and credibility which it enjoyed leading up to the 1960's.

According to Einstein, the universe, including humans, is nothing but energy and frequencies. Professor Stephen Hawking, the "Black Hole" physicist, has said that the future development of medicine lies with treatments based on light and colour.

At the atomic level, a living cell is a matrix of vibrating atoms with electrons spinning and exchanging orbits at the speed of light. There is an additional unexplained factor, the "life force" element. This element is one of the major missing links in the western medical approach. The colour of cells reflects the frequency of their vibrational rate. When living cells die, their colour changes. The human body is a vibrating atomic field of several billions of living and dying cells. Living cells have a specific vibrational rate or frequency. Good health is radiant and can be witnessed by all. If too many of the body's cells become diseased, we become ill. At the atomic level, there is a change in frequency and colour. Diseased cells, that is, cells with low biological energy and vibrational rates, are easy targets for infectious organisms to invade.

Disease exists at the atomic level. Changes take place in the vibrational rate and orbital exchanges of the valence electrons which make up cells. The frequency of the cell changes, which in turn affects the cell's life force.

As far as promoting healing is concerned, sluggish cells, organs and glands which are vibrating too slowly will benefit from any method which will increase and unify their rhythms. Conversely, cells, organs and glands which are excited or stressed will benefit from any method which will reduce and unify their vibrational activity. Today, using various electronic methods, valence electrons can be easily modulated without any physical or invasive contact with the patient's body. And what is even more exciting is that this type of energy medicine does not use the shotgun approach, it is non-invasive, non-systemic and will target the precise parts of the patient's body which are in need of treatment. This spares the patient from suffering the debilitating side effects which drug therapies and surgery induce.

This book demonstrates the clinical application and development of numerous innovative procedures which produce astoundingly consistent and rapid results. The claims are supported with case studies that are abstracts from various practitioners' patient files. All of the cases are genuine. The majority are all chronic cases which have failed to respond to orthodox medicines or psychological therapies. Many of the patients included in this book had resorted to alternative and complementary therapies in an attempt to find a cure without success. Within these case studies of electronic gem lamp therapy the placebo effect cannot be credited for the results. The placebo effect does not come into the equations. These patients had ample opportunities to get well with the various medications and therapies which their doctors, hospitals and therapists had prescribed. The fact that these simple and economical procedures have worked where other expensive therapies had failed is what makes the cases so extraordinary.

The Assemblage Point and other procedures outlined will have a profound effect on all conventional medical practices, many of which will have to be modified and overhauled to include the new medical and physiological discoveries outlined. Many hundreds of medical, psychological and other technical publications, and the belief systems and practices surrounding them, when read in the light of the Assemblage Point factor, are now obsolete. Since it is unethical to deny treatment to a patient when it is available, now that the human Assemblage Point diagnostic and correction procedures have been published, medical researchers and practitioners who choose to ignore it and do not take into account their patient's Assemblage Point are leaving themselves open to obvious criticisms in the future.

Apart from the obvious benefits for the ordinary person, the contents of this book are of immense professional importance to surgeons, physicians, psychiatrists, psychologists, alternative and complementary therapists, social and rehabilitation workers. The book also presents enormous financial benefits for insurance companies, corporate bodies, businesses and competitive sporting activities.

More remarkably, the exposure of the Assemblage Point factor is greatly accelerating and reinforcing the increasing inclinations of the general public to depart from their, now hazardous, traditional trusting patient attitude and to take control of their health and personal, social and spiritual development.

Dr. Jon Whale

August 2000

For our American readers, please note that when the British author of this book refers to 'myalgic encephomyelitis' or 'M.E.' he is also referring to 'chronic fatigue syndrome'.

THE MISSING LINK:

THE ASSEMBLAGE POINT OF MAN

It is a scientific fact that energy systems are assembled from an epicentre. Galaxies, stars, planets, molecules and atoms are all energy systems which oscillate. By virtue of the fact that they are oscillating, they all have a centre of rotation. Other types of oscillating energy systems, such as electricity generating stations, radio and television transmission stations or mobile telephones also have an epicentre. Gravity and magnetism are examples of force and energy fields upon which our lives depend, yet the eye cannot see them. These energy fields radiate from a spinning central point called the epicentre. The Earth's magnetic field extends into space. If we could see it, it would look like a massive doughnut and, like a doughnut, it has a hole at the north and south poles, the axis of its epicentre. Radio waves, infrared, ultra violet, X-rays and gamma rays are all invisible waves that make up the Frequency Spectrum; their origins can all be traced back to their epicentre. The human eye is sensitive to a narrow band of frequencies called light, and can only see a minute percentage of the frequency spectrum, which radiates from our Sun. From this perspective, we are all ignorant of what is actually going on in the unseen universe around us.

When white light strikes an object, the surface of the object vibrates at a specific frequency which is equivalent to the colour seen. For example, the colour of the light reflected by the metal gold is predominantly yellow, therefore gold's natural vibration wave length is 590 nanometres or around 612 billion cycles per second. Gold absorbs all other frequencies or colours except yellow. By contrast, the metal silver has the capacity to vibrate at and reflect all colours or frequencies of the light spectrum and many other frequencies besides. It is for this reason we use silver metal to plate the glass of mirrors. When we look into a mirror, the silver provides us with a true reflection of the colours of our physical form, it also reflect images of us which we cannot see but which can be detected by electronic instruments.

The narrow band of frequencies of white light is made up of millions of different frequencies and each individual frequency represents a different colour or tone. Modern semiconductor solar panels collect light and convert it into electricity or electron flow. Television cameras collect light and convert it into electronic pulses that are decoded by the television set to reproduce the picture. The eye collects light and converts it into electrical pulses which travel along the optic nerve and are decoded by the brain. Very few of us comprehend that what we see of the world around us is not the real thing, it is a model or an image constructed inside our brain. The brain's model of the external reality is censored by our individual expectations and beliefs. The brain's model of reality can be seriously distorted by intimidation, illness, fever, drugs or toxins.

Although our eyes cannot see individual electrons or atoms, they can see the frequency at which electrons vibrate at in the form of colour. However, the human body can feel electron flow; most of us have experienced the shock caused by static electricity from cars or nylon carpets. Where electrons flow there is electrical current, where there is current, then there are voltages and relating magnetic fields. Conversely, where there are electromagnetic fields, they will induce electron flow from one atom to the next, generating electricity.

The atoms of the molecules which make up a living cell rhythmically exchange their outer circle or shell of orbiting electrons with electrons from adjacent atoms. A molecule is a group of atoms which are linked by the outer shell of orbiting electrons. The molecule of water, for example, is constructed of two atoms of hydrogen gas and one atom of oxygen. The electrons of the hydrogen and oxygen atoms rhythmically exchange their orbits at very high speeds, and this exchange of each atom's electrons ties the oxygen atom and the two hydrogen atoms together, forming water.

The circulating high speed dance of the outer shell of electrons in a molecule continually defines and maintains the molecule's structure. Living cells are made up of a large structure of interactive molecules. Within the living cell, electron flow creates small magnetic fields. The health and vitality of a person is reflected in the flow of energy in their cellular body. The overall flow in the body creates a larger magnetic field surrounding it. This field has a number of smaller modulated fields inside it. These fields relate to the functions of the internal organs and glands. There are electron flow pathways or channels, which extend from the brain, to all the organs and glands, and throughout the body, to the hands and feet. The human body is a miraculous system of some 100 billion individual living and dying cells.

Over one hundred years ago science demonstrated that surrounding every atom is a cloud of electrons. This fact proves that everything in the material universe, including the human body, consists of electrical energy. The human body is a complex electrical energy system and, over a century later, this scientific fact has largely been ignored by medical science. Therefore it is not surprising that medical science has yet to discover the epicentre of the human energy system. The flow of electricity in the human body controls and affects this rhythmic exchange of electrons. Emotional traumas, drugs and infections, for example, can completely disrupt the body's natural rhythms and levels of electron exchange - we literally experience an emotional electric shock. The effects can be measured and recorded by sensitive electronic voltage or current meters and various electronic medical chart recorders. Besides the body's electricity, there is an unquantifiable and unseen energy factor which can exercise its will over the body's 100 billion individual living cells. This is the life force or spirit entity that is part of every living human.

Diseases of The Second Body

Surrounding and permeating every cell of a living person is a vibrating energy field. It is an egg-shaped pressure field which contains and characterises our individual consciousness and state of being from that of others and the universe at large. In other words, we all are an individual energy system that can, to a large extent, move around and function independently, under the direction of our will. Our physical body is encapsulated in an oscillating energy field which has a boundary. The characteristics of each person's physical and psychological makeup will be reflected in the frequency and extent of their energy field. Other descriptions for this field are the human aura or electromagnetic body; some scientists call it the unified field. Every living person has an oscillating energy field and scientifically and, in reality, all of us have an energy epicentre. The human energy field epicentre is a very bright spot of high energy which the trained person can feel or see. The vortex or epicentre of the human energy system is called the Assemblage Point of man. It is called the Assemblage Point because we are assembled in the womb from the umbilical cord that connects us to the placenta of our mother. The major input of energy enters the developing foetus via the navel.

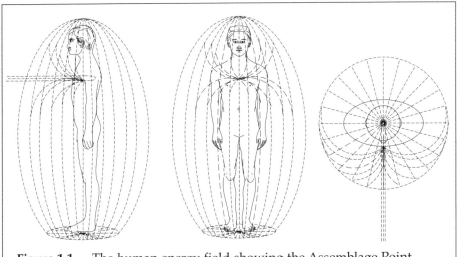

Figure 1.1   The human energy field showing the Assemblage Point.

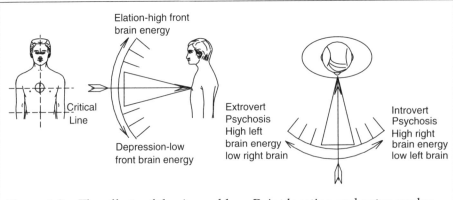

Figure 1.2   The effects of the Assemblage Point location and entry angles on brain energy.

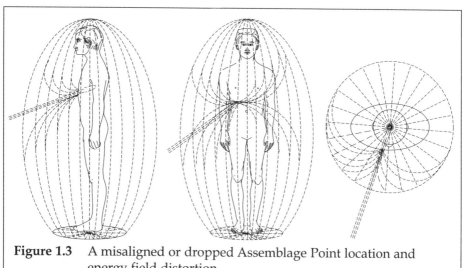

Figure 1.3   A misaligned or dropped Assemblage Point location and energy field distortion.

At the time of birth, the Assemblage Point is positioned at the navel area. However, the Assemblage Point location for the physically and mentally healthy adult is close to the thymus gland in the centre of the chest. In someone who is suffering from mental or physical symptoms or disease, the Assemblage Point will be found in a different location. As we approach our time of death, our Assemblage Point moves down towards the navel. This knowledge has profound implications for world health and the advancement of current medical models, therapies and practice.

Misalignment Causes Mental and Physical Health Problems

For most healthy people, the idea that how we behave and how we feel is beyond our rational control is preposterous. For those of us who have experienced a serious physical accident, disease, fever, tragedy, violent intimidation, drug overdose, acute stress or depression, this idea is acceptable and can be easily comprehended. Under such circumstances many people undergo a personality change, often accompanied by unfamiliar physical symptoms and illness.

Physical fatigue, emotional exhaustion or disease can very easily bring about an involuntary shift of the Assemblage Point, a situation that can be exceptionally dangerous.

Sufferers experience that "something" deep inside them has changed. Although they can remember how they behaved and felt before the incident, it is impossible for them to return to their former self. That indescribable "something" deep inside all of us which can suddenly shift, changing our whole perception of reality including our physical health, is the location of the Assemblage Point.

The Assemblage Point is a vortex of high energy in the Electromagnetic Body. There are three categories of types of Assemblage Point shifts and these are:

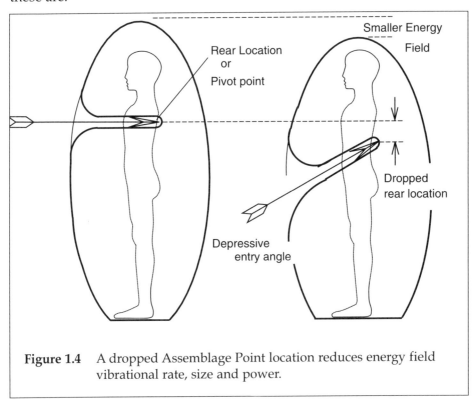

Figure 1.4   A dropped Assemblage Point location reduces energy field vibrational rate, size and power.

1) A movement or change in angle
2) A shift or change in angle and location
3) A shift in depth or a change in angle, location and size.

The Assemblage Point is a vortex of high energy in the Electromagnetic Body. It is the location of the Assemblage Point that "dictates" how we behave, feel and perceive the world. Its location influences our conscious reality and greatly affects physical and mental health. Every one of us has an Assemblage Point and it is very easy to locate. The procedure for locating and correcting it is quick, simple and painless. Manipulation of the location of the Assemblage Point can change our state of consciousness, increase our biological energy levels and improve general health. Familiarity with its location and performing regular adjustments to it can accelerate personal development and improve mental and physical efficiency. Correct alignment of the Energy Body with the physical body are vital for our physical and mental well-being. Figure 1.1 shows the correct alignment.

Violence, intimidation, bereavement, shock, accidents, trauma, drugs, toxins and illness can easily dislocate the Energy Body's alignment. Depending on the severity and direction of the misalignment, various psychological and physical symptoms will be present. Gross misalignment of the Energy Body is present in depression, numerous psychotic and psychological disorders, drug and alcohol addiction, toxicity, leukaemia, cancer, auto immune defence syndrome (A.I.D.S.),

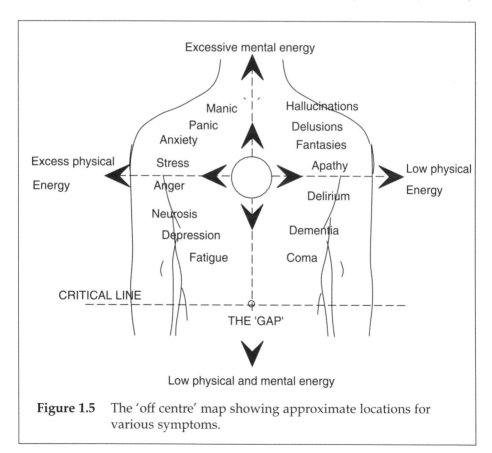

Figure 1.5   The 'off centre' map showing approximate locations for various symptoms.

myalgic encephalomyelitis (M.E.), multiple sclerosis (M.S.), post natal depression, schizophrenia, epilepsy, senile dementia (Alzheimer's), coma, Parkinsonism, etc.. It is a simple matter to find out the alignment of a person's Energy Body by locating the Assemblage Point.

For optimum health and vitality, energies in the left and right sides of the brain should be equal and the Electromagnetic Field equally distributed about the body's central meridian line. The ideal location for the Assemblage Point is the central position, shown in figure 1.1. In this position balanced biological energy flows around the central nervous system and the many organs and glands function in harmony. This ideal alignment is rare. With most people the Assemblage Point will be found entering on the right side of the chest's central meridian line; this is due to the excessive left brain activity resulting in physical and mental activity, which is demanded by today's stressful life style. Drugs, toxins, illness, accidents and emotional trauma are the most common causes of misalignment. Once misalignment has occurred, though not impossible, it is very difficult, to re-establish the original position by one's own efforts or by orthodox medical therapies.

Neither orthodox nor complementary medicine has the diagnostic or treatment procedures to correct Electromagnetic Body alignment. However, realignment is a simple procedure which takes a few minutes to execute. Misalignment causes mild to serious imbalances of energy distribution in the brain and nervous system, upsetting endocrine and hormone functions. The symptoms directly relate to the location and entry angle as in figure 1.2. The further the location is outside the shaded area in figure 1.2, the more acute the listed symptoms. Figure 1.5. gives the approximate positions for various physical and psychological symptoms. The symptoms experienced will vary according to the location and the angle of entry. Severe misalignment causes acute disturbances in the functioning of the organs and glands. Over a period of time, biological damage can occur. A dropped Assemblage Point causes energy field distortion, lower vibrational rate and lower energy field power. This effect is shown in figures 1.3 and 1.4.

Today, psychiatrists, psychologists and other health professionals do not employ Assemblage Point location in their diagnosis or correct gross misalignment. The alignment of the Electromagnetic Body controls the way we feel, think and our perception of reality. It is almost impossible to correct alignment by psychoanalysis, talking, thinking or by medication. Therefore the currently employed usual method is to give drugs to relieve or mask the symptoms caused by misalignment. Shifting the location of the Assemblage Point and adjusting the angle will alter the state of human consciousness. The following two case studies illustrate the profound connection between health and the patient's Assemblage Point location. In the first case, the Assemblage Point location is low on the right side of the chest and in the second case it is on the left side of the patient's chest.

Case 1. Clinical Depression following Concussion

Tony B, aged 13, March 1996. Four years previously, Tony had fallen backwards from a high stone wall at his school. He had lost consciousness and was hospitalised for concussion. He suffered headaches and vomiting after regaining consciousness. Later he developed alopecia and eczema at the site of his head injury (parietal bone left side). Tony's mother reported that he had been a very energetic and extrovert boy before the accident. However, since the accident he had not attended school; he had developed agoraphobia and insomnia, and hardly ever left his bedroom. Over the years he had seen many specialists for various examinations, X-rays and scans. He had received extensive treatment from homoeopaths, osteopaths and a physiotherapist, with some slight improvements. More recently, his psychiatrist had voiced the opinion that he was suffering from M.E. and that he would have to go into hospital for drug tests. He was receiving antidepressants and anti-inflammatory analgesics.

On examination, the location of his Assemblage Point was found to be very low down on the right side, just above the critical line at the navel. His depressed attitude, slurred speech, monotone voice and hunched posture were confirmation of the low location. Tony admitted that he was always staring at the ground. He complained of having no energy and extensive pains. Tony was a co-operative patient, so shifting his Assemblage Point up and across to the central location was easy. He agreed to ancillary treatment with electronic gem therapy lamps.

Two weeks later, on his second visit, his mother reported he had been cycling and attending local social functions and that he had been sleeping far better. Tony told us that he had experienced much more energy, but over the last few days he complained that it had "dropped away". Examination revealed that his Assemblage Point had partially dropped. This is normal with long-term misalignment. He received treatment similar to that on his first visit. On his third visit, he arrived on his bicycle, having cycled 12 miles. His complexion, energy, speech and posture were much better. His Assemblage Point had slipped down a little. Tony said that his psychiatrist had noted a significant change in him.

Tony's alignment was corrected five times over a 3 month period. Each time the correction distance was less, and the interval between visits was greater. Six months later, Tony was free from pain, sleeping normally, off all medication, and was taking up extrovert activities, including archery and fishing. Given the length of time that he had been ill, his recovery was remarkable. He left behind 4 years of negative states of consciousness, which had considerably disrupted his education and personal development. Tony's case is a classic one of "dropped Assemblage Point".

Case 2. Paediatric Psychosis (Autism)

A 6 year old boy. June 1997. This boy was diagnosed with disintegrative psychosis, a variety of autism which possibly develops after vaccination, particularly that given for measles. The reasoning for this is as follows: an autistic youngster seems to be very "out of contact" or dissociated from the world and "dreamy". He (usually a male patient) is very introverted into the right brain hemisphere. If we could use electronic gem lamp therapy to accelerate left brain and retard right brain activity, we may be able to appropriately stimulate the logical reasoning faculties. Accordingly, he was given a one week programme of diamond, citrine and ruby to the left cranial hemisphere and emerald combined with sapphire to the right side of the brain. This was further refined by using Beta frequencies (inducing high brain activity) of around 15 Hz to the left side and retarding, soothing Theta frequencies (3.3 Hz) to the right hemisphere. The penetration was lowered to minimal wattage, in order not to crossover and inadvertently stimulate the opposite side of the brain. Within days he began vocalising well and within a month was forming intelligible sentences. He continued to make rapid progress. He has since learned to use a computer keyboard and happily spends hours amusing himself with electronic games, which, of course, require considerable left brain dexterity. His mother also reports that he has learned to integrate well with his peers.

Left and Right Sided Awareness

It is now a proven medical fact that when the left nostril is deliberately blocked and we breathe in and out through the right nostril only, the left side of the brain becomes more electrically active, compared to that of the right brain. Scientific research has proved this with infrared pictures and other types of brain scanning and monitoring devices. It is also a medical fact that injuries to the left side of the brain affect the muscular co-ordination of the right side of the body and that injuries to the right side of the brain affect the left side of the body (see figure 1.6).

A not very well known example of the use of this knowledge concerns sinus problems. Should the right or left nostril be obstructed by the sinus, applying pressure under the opposite arm pit will cause the nostril to clear. Massaging the large toe on the opposite foot will also clear the nostril. This simple and effective exercise proves that there is a nervous connection between our nostrils and our opposite large toes and arms. When most people first try these exercises out on themselves, they are astounded. There are many people who have undergone surgery for blocked sinuses, when actually the root of their problems is a blockage in the electrical energy flow of the physical body. In most cases, even after surgery the nostrils remain obstructed.

Scientific researchers using electro-encephalographs to monitor and record the electrical activities of the human brain have demonstrated that the left and right sides of the human brain have distinctly different functions. The left brain activities are currently thought to be: logical thinking and extrovert pursuits, whereas the right brain's activities are associated with emotional feelings and introvert spatial conceptions. Medical researchers have not been able to adequately explain the reasons for the distinctly different functions of each half of our brain. However, if we take a larger overview of the human body and include in this overview the electrical and chemical activities associated with each side of the body, then the reasons become clearly evident.

If the left side of the brain is damaged by a blood clot or internal bleeding, resulting from a stroke or head injury, the right side of the body can become paralysed. The left brain controls the right side of the body and, as everyone knows, the liver is located on the right side of an adult's body. Whilst the spleen, and to some extent also the heart, are located on the left side of the body, which relates to the right side of the brain. The

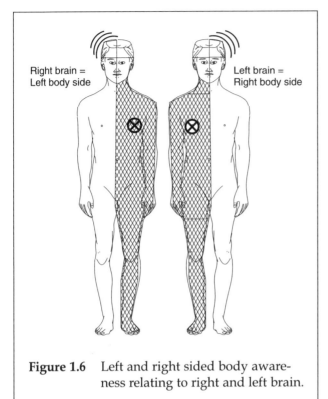

**Right brain =
Left body side**

**Left brain =
Right body side**

Figure 1.6 Left and right sided body awareness relating to right and left brain.

liver has many important functions and its healthy activity is essential for life. The most urgent of its functions is keeping a steady concentration of glucose in the blood to replace what is consumed as fuel. The brain keeps no stores at all and quickly dies if supplies from the liver are cut off.

As all stressful or intimidating situations place a heavy demand for glucose on the liver, and the liver is on the right side of the body, the situation is reflected by excessive left brain electrical activity. Excessive electrical energy in the left side of the brain has for some years now been scientifically associated with stress. Accompanying stress are raised blood pressure, increased heart rate and muscle tension, together with increased levels of adrenaline in the blood. Stressful situations prepare the body for the extrovert activities of "fight" or "flight". Intimidation and stress unbalance the chemical and electrical functions in the body and brain. This imbalance moves the Assemblage Point to the right side of the body reflecting the increased electrical activity in the left brain and liver. Almost everyone who experiences a seriously stressful or intimidating incident will take several days or even months to recover. In extreme cases, the person experiences post traumatic shock syndrome and may never recover their original Assemblage Point location.

Brain Frequencies And Health

Assemblage Point location affects the left and right brain energy levels and the brain's predominant operating frequencies. A person's state of health and consciousness is directly related to their brain frequencies. The brain frequencies of panic are very much faster than sleep (figure 1.7).

1) Very fast brain frequencies greater than 25 Hz or cycles per second produce corresponding states of anxiety, panic, anger and psychosis. This range is called High Beta and if sustained for long periods, it is dangerous for our health and can cause physical damage.

2) Fast brain frequencies in the range 14 - 25 HZ relate to attention focussed on external affairs and are called Beta. In the long term, excessive preoccupation with activities which induce or require the brain and body to operate at Beta frequencies can be hazardous due to the physical stress they impart.

3) Medium speed brain frequencies between 7.8 - 14 HZ produce a relaxed state of consciousness, with attention divided between internal and external activities. This range of frequencies is called Alpha and is often referred to as the meditation frequencies. Meditation lowers brain frequencies from the stressful Beta range and can, for some people with a predisposition for symptoms associated with High Beta waves, resolve their problems.

4) The slow brain frequency range of between 3.2 - 7.8 HZ produces a wide range of internal mental phenomena. This frequency range is called Theta. The attention is directed to internal brain activities such as dreaming, trance and other so called mystical states. Hypnosis is a method of inducing Theta states of consciousness where the brain is very susceptible to outside programming. In these states of consciousness emotional and physical pain are substantially reduced.

5) Very slow brain frequencies of 0.1 - 3.2 HZ are related to states of unconsciousness, deep sleep, anaesthesia and coma, where there is an absence of feelings or pain.

The body's network of nerves transmit modulations of the brain frequencies to every part of the body. Therefore, when the mind is stressed or relaxed, the physical body follows in sympathy. Indeed, the nervous system is a finely tuned feedback system. In situations where the physical body is stressed by illness or injury then the brain frequencies increase and we experience a related mental discomfort.

1. Assemblage Point locations on the right side of the body (figure 1.6) can be uncomfortable and distressing. They induce and are associated with an increase in left brain activity and Beta brain frequencies together with a preoccupation with extrovert attention and activities. This is accompanied by higher blood pressure, heart rate and adrenaline levels and excessive physical and nervous energy.

2. Conversely, locations on the left body side (figure 1.10) induce and are associated with an increase in right brain activity and Theta brain frequencies, together with a preoccupation with introvert attention and activities. This is accompanied with lower blood pressure, heart rate and increased levels of endorphin, the body's natural pain killer.

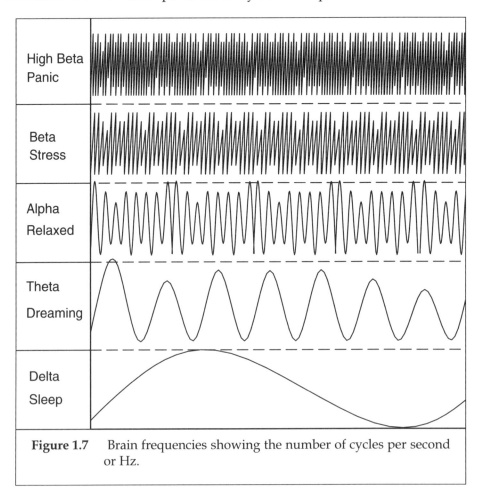

Figure 1.7   Brain frequencies showing the number of cycles per second or Hz.

3. Central Assemblage Point locations (figure 1.1) are very beneficial for health, and personal and social development. They induce balanced brain and bodily activities and Alpha brain frequencies, together with relaxed and balanced internal and external attention. This is accompanied by normal blood pressure, heart rate and balanced bodily functions.

4. Low Assemblage Point locations (figures 1.9 and 1.11] are very dangerous to health. They induce and are associated with low frontal brain energy and low Alpha and Theta brain frequencies. When the Assemblage Point is on the right side, the symptoms are physical and mental depression. When the Assemblage Point location is low on the left side, it is associated with catatonic symptoms and coma. The blood pressure and heart rate will be slow and weak and the muscle tension will be low.

5. High locations on the right or left are dangerous to health and society. They reflect in an increase in frontal brain energy and excessively high Beta brain frequencies. When the Assemblage Point is located high on the far right, it induces extrovert psychotic behaviour. When it is high on the far left, introvert psychotic behaviour is experienced.

The Assemblage Point Location and its angle of alignment affect the state of the patient's consciousness and the way their internal organs function. Manually shifting the Assemblage Point is the fast way back to normality, high biological energy and improved mental and physical health. Realignment should be done as soon as possible after the incident that caused the misalignment, to minimise the possibility of physical damage and disease manifesting as a result of long term imbalances in biological energy distribution. Even in patients who have been sick for a long time, realignment can make a significant contribution to their recovery. Where detrimental Assemblage Point locations are associated with, or are perhaps due to the presence of, toxins in the patient's body, or there is physical damage or gross malfunctions of any of the organs, these problems will also have to be addressed. The procedures for this are covered in later chapters.

The Stress of The Shift to The Right

This is the most commonly found misalignment. Symptoms are compulsive mental and physical activity and are illustrated by the following case studies.

Case 3. Chronic Panic Attacks

Clare W, aged 18. September 1996. Clare reported that she was experiencing panic attacks which had started years before when she was attending junior school. She had been seeing a clinical psychologist since breaking her leg when having an attack. Her Assemblage Point was checked and found to be on the far right side of the chest at an acute angle, passing through the heart. There was also a shadow location 8 cm higher up, in the location for panic. The shadow location and her Assemblage Point were joined and shifted to the centre. Just over a year later, a letter was received from her. She wrote that she had not experienced any attacks since her treatment, and that she had now gained complete control over herself and her life.

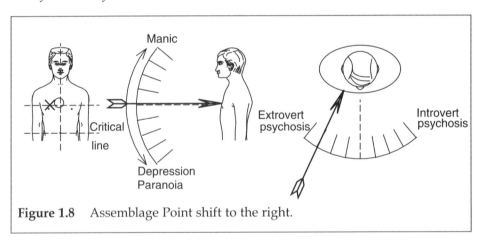

Figure 1.8　Assemblage Point shift to the right.

Case 4. Executive Stress

Ms R.J., Business Manager. September 1998. The patient reported, "I had been experiencing a very stressful time at work. I had been working 6 days each week until late at night for many months. I had had more than my fair share of problems with junior staff. Due to this, I was drinking and smoking too much, and finding it very difficult to relax. I had had my Assemblage Point shifted to the centre 2 years previously, so I knew what to expect. However, its location was further on the right this time. The shift made me feel much less stressed and my pulse rate was much slower afterwards. Most noticeable was my breathing; I had a great feeling of relief and I could breath more deeply and freely; my cigarette and alcohol consumption spontaneously reduced, due to the fact that I felt completely centred again".

The medical diagnosis for those having their Assemblage Point in the above patient's location is stress. Excessive feelings of anxiety, panic or anger are indicators of this location. These are associated with High Beta brain-wave frequencies in the left brain. The Assemblage Point moves to the right side of the chest as shown in figure 1.8.

In paranoia the location and angle are to the right and down. In mania the location is high right and the angle is upwards. Manic depression and schizophrenia are associated with oscillations and splits in the Assemblage Point location. On the extreme right there are endless visions of physical activity, violence, killing and sensuality.

Intimidation, worry, overwork, insomnia, cocaine, L.S.D., amphetamines, antidepressants and excessive caffeine can drive the stationary Assemblage Point to the far right. In this position various physical symptoms medically connected with stress will appear. Energy demands are high and sleep will be problematic. High Beta frequency brain activity is present. The attention is external and the awareness of the physical body is attenuated. Locations further to the right cause psychotic behaviour that can include violence and sexual deviations. Left brain energy will be high, right brain low. From this position, drugs, illness or emotional trauma can cause complete exhaustion of the nervous system. The Assemblage Point then drops down towards the critical line as shown in figure 1.9. M.E. is a disease with this location, the Assemblage Point always entering the patient from a low angle up through the liver. Shifting the Assemblage Point to the centre will give immediate relief. Regular shifting will recondition the nervous system back to normal, thus reducing or removing the patient's dependence on drugs.

The Dangers of The Shift Below

This is a dangerous, uncomfortable and distressing location. The indications are very low mental and physical energy with acute psychological instability and physiological disturbances. Impaired functions of endocrine glands and organs may develop. Frontal brain energy will be low. From this location it is virtually impossible to recover without realignment of the Assemblage Point. As the Assemblage Point's rear location or pivot point drops down from the shoulder blade area, muscular coordination becomes affected.

Case 5. Feeling of Detachment from Body, Low Energy, Anxiety and Depression

Tony S, aged 24, April 1997. Tony had been ill for 8 years. He complained of feeling detached from his body, anxious, depressed and having no energy. This condition had started when he first began work at 15 and he had been unable to work for the past several years. He had attended a psychiatrist, psychologist and hypnotherapist. He had also tried acupuncture, healers and a psychoanalyst, throughout which time he reported that his condition had got worse. It required five attempts to successfully shift his Assemblage Point up, from the M.E. location just below the liver. Tony required three more corrections over a 2 month period, during which he made steady progress to recovery.

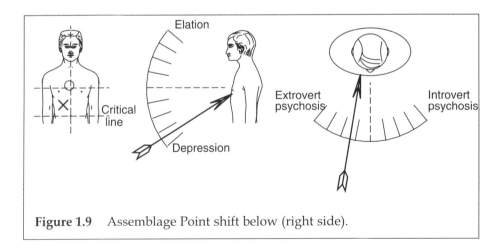

Figure 1.9 Assemblage Point shift below (right side).

With this location, serious psychiatric or physical illness will often be present. Diseases associated are auto immune disease syndrome (A.I.D.S.), cancer, meningitis, cerebral thrombosis, apoplexy, clinical depression, post natal depression, myalgic encephalomyelitis (M.E. syndrome) and multiple sclerosis (M.S. syndrome). As the Assemblage Point moves towards the critical line, the symptoms become worse. Beta activity will mostly be absent. Distressing feelings and emotions are prevalent. Sympathy, placation or chastisement do not help. Toxic material, heavy metals, chemotherapy drugs, poisoning, head injury, drugs, attempted suicide, solvent abuse, violent intimidation, physical shock, electric shock, long term exposure to strong electromagnetic and high voltage electrostatic fields, anoxia, infections and disease can drive the Assemblage Point to this location. Antidepressants will not correct this location. Shifting the location up and over to the centre will immediately alleviate the symptoms. Vibrational levels will increase and more energy will be available even if physiological disease is present. The natural healing process will accelerate.

The Trap of the Shift to the Left

Irrational preoccupation with daydreaming, fantasy, hallucinations and melancholia are the most common indicators for this location. L.S.D. and other hallucinogenic drugs can cause a shift to the left (or in any direction). Pseudo religious cult brainwashing methods unconsciously shift the location to the left side (figure 1.10).

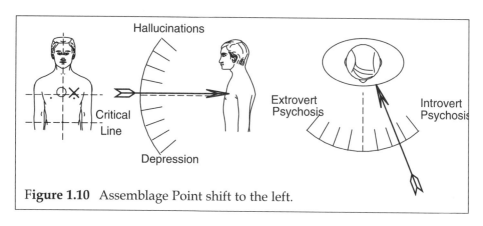

Figure 1.10 Assemblage Point shift to the left.

Case 6. Agoraphobia and Clinical Depression

Mr N.O. aged 32, September 1989.This man, a professional sculptor and artist in the film and television industry, had not attended work for over a year. He had developed agoraphobia after ingesting a quantity of L.S.D. at a party. After the effects of the drug had worn off, he became increasingly distressed with work and travelling on the underground railway to London. He was signed off sick by his doctor and attended psychiatric therapy. His situation continued to deteriorate and he spent most of his days dreaming and making drawings of strange science fiction situations in black ink. He attended for Assemblage Point correction at the suggestion of one of his friends. Examination revealed that his Assemblage Point was on the left side of his chest. His Assemblage Point was moved to the right side of his chest and he attended for several more monthly corrections. He eventually made a full recovery back to his former health and activities.

Locations on the extreme left side are associated with visions and experiences of spirituality, religion and God. If the location of the shift is minimal, the results are explained as fantasies of the mind. If the shift is considerable, the results are called hallucinations. Shifting the Assemblage Point to right of the centre will return behaviour to normal. It will increase left brain energy, Beta frequencies and rationality.

Senile dementia, autism, Down's Syndrome and coma are examples where the location will be around the area shown in figure 1.11. In the early stages of these diseases regular checks and correction of the Assemblage Point may slow the progress. Astute doctors and clinicians will in future reverse these diseases by combining Assemblage Point realignment with other therapies. For energy medicine treatment of senile dementia and autism see Chapter Seven.

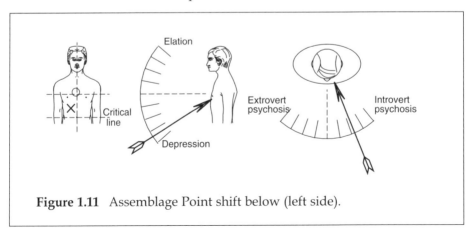

Figure 1.11 Assemblage Point shift below (left side).

The Missing Link to The Limitations of Western Medicine

In the womb, the foetus is assembled via the umbilical cord and the Assemblage Point of the unborn child is at the navel. With birth, the cord is severed and the baby's Assemblage Point moves upwards from the navel to the chest area. Over the course of the first seven years of our life the Stationary Assemblage Point moves up the centre line from the navel and becomes situated in a predetermined position somewhere in the right chest area.

Just below the navel is an aperture caused prior to birth by the umbilical cord. It is a naturally weak area in the field called "the Gap". Death occurs instantaneously, when the Assemblage Point drops to below the navel, causing the Electromagnetic Field to collapse. While the Assemblage Point is above the navel line death cannot occur. Preventing the Assemblage Point from dropping to the Gap, will postpone death. The ethical controversy as to whether or not a patient in a coma should have their life support system disconnected is easily resolved with Assemblage Point diagnosis. If the patient's Assemblage Point can be located, i.e. the patient has an Assemblage Point, then he or she is still alive and it would be unethical to disconnect their life support. If their Assemblage Point cannot be found then the life support system can ethically be unplugged from its electricity supply.

The human spirit departs from the body at the precise moment at which the Assemblage Point traverses the navel meridian line. The Assemblage Point is the missing energy link connecting the human soul with the physical body. This connection is absent in the current Western medical model. Many of the current dilemmas and criticisms which Western medicine are now experiencing can be easily resolved with stringent application of Assemblage Point diagnosis and correction procedures. Not only are the Assemblage Point diagnostics and correction principles applicable to mental and physical disease, but central location can also dramatically improve mental and physical efficiency. This induces stable and efficient states of well being which are very desirable. In the future, greater public awareness of the Assemblage Point will have profound beneficial reverberations for financial, social and political health on a global basis.

chapter 2

THE KEY TO THE PARADOXES OF LIFE

To perform a complicated mathematical task or sit an important examination requires concentrated effort and can with most people induce real physical and emotional stress. The mental functions demanded necessitate long periods of logical brain activity at Beta brain wave frequencies accompanied by excessive muscle tension, all of which place great demands on the liver. Many of us have experienced diarrhoea and can remember all of the school toilets being engaged prior to an important test or examination.

Excessive mental concentration of a worrying or stressful nature will cause the Assemblage Point to drift to the right side of the chest. Assemblage Point locations on the right side of the chest are inherently unstable. This is due an attenuated awareness of the body and the excessive production of adrenaline. Under these conditions, it is all too easy to ignore the body's requirements, for example, by not eating or sleeping properly, or drinking and smoking too much. Continued to an excess, the biological energy reserves become depleted. This causes more instability of the Assemblage Point location, which is potentially dangerous.

The Search for Enlightenment

Biological energy management has fast become a preoccupation of modern times. Currently there are hundreds of different schools and centres, teaching a wide range of physical, mental, mystical and esoteric disciplines for personal growth and development. Many of them employ, to a greater or lesser degree, methods for the development and management of biological energy. Meditation, various types of yoga, judo, acupuncture, Tai Chi, Reiki and self hypnosis are examples. Many systems combine physical exercises, sexual constraints, deep breathing, concentrated visualisation using sound, colour and symbols and dietary and environmental controls. With a little practice, almost anyone can learn how to accumulate reserves of biological energy. After some time, the student can learn how to control and direct the energy around their body. Some schools teach their student various types of methods using the hands, to direct and send their accumulated biological energy around others, for the purpose of healing.

There are numerous meditation schools and centres and some of them are major players in the biological energy management business. One particular international meditation faction teaches an effortless meditation method said to relieve stress and trauma. The method also claims to promote personal health, self and social development. Practitioners meditate by mentally repeating a special sound or mental vibration, called a mantra. Once in the morning and again in the evening, the practitioner sits upright for fifteen to twenty minutes. Each time the meditator observes that he or she is "thinking", she mentally reverberates her personal mantra in her mind. Mantras used are often words such: "Harhim", "Shrim" or "Kharim". The mantra is mentally reverberated in such a way that it "washes away" the normal thinking process (see Figure 2.1). Some meditation practitioners can attain a profound state of physical and mental relaxation. Regular practice integrates the right and left brain energy levels and can induce Alpha brain wave states of relaxed attention throughout the day. During meditation, the practitioners often report visual dreaming episodes. This suggests that this particular method stimulates right brain activity. This type of personal mantra meditation is used to modulate the brain wave frequencies down to a slower rate. Regular practitioners can, within a few minutes, slow their brain wave frequencies from stressful High Beta (25 Hz) down to dreaming Theta frequencies (3.3 Hz). Most newcomers can take a period of ten to twenty minutes to get down to a relaxed dreamy state, as illustrated in figure 2.1.. Adrenaline and blood pressure levels are significantly reduced, along with use of alcohol, stimulants and tranquillisers. The physical and mental benefits are enormous and the effects have been recorded with electro encephalogram recorders (E.E.G.) and other devices such as the "Mind Mirror", which is attached to the head via skin electrodes and wires. These instruments can record and display brain frequencies of a person, while they are sleeping, dreaming, meditating, or performing a mental task.

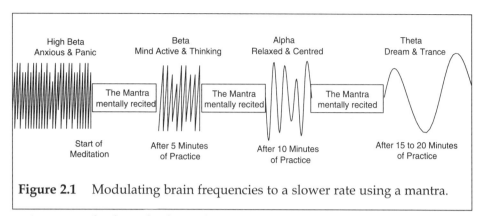

Figure 2.1 Modulating brain frequencies to a slower rate using a mantra.

As stress depletes biological energy, spending long periods of time in the relaxed states of Theta and Alpha brain frequencies, allows biological energy reserves to accumulate, producing an excess. Biological energy reserves can be very substantially increased with special breathing techniques and concentrated visualisation exercises, as well as diet and celibacy.

There is a great deal of misunderstanding concerning sexual energy, the spiritual path and celibacy. For most people, especially for older males, sexual orgasm almost always induces sleep. As with sexual intercourse, energy builds up and then is expelled in the orgasm phase. It is obvious that our biological energy levels can be deliberately increased by stimulating sexual energy but refraining from or retaining the orgasm. These techniques are called Tantric yoga and these days they are used by some people to increase their creativity. The methods also can make dramatic improvements in personal health and in one's relationships. Orgasm retention provides much more energy than does celibacy, this is because the practitioner deliberately stirs up and controls nature's creative force and substantial quantities of personal energy can be accumulated and used for other purposes.

Excess energy can be directed around one's physical body and that of others to produce a wide variety of euphoric and other states of consciousness. For most of us, our excess biological energy reserves are expressed in our work, sports, affections, sexual activities and other creative hobbies or pastimes. As previously mentioned some people can, using their hands, direct excess biological energy around others for the purpose of healing. This type of healing is often called 'spiritual healing', some spiritual healers claim that they are a special channel through which a 'higher power' or God works to heal others who are less fortunate.

Spiritual healers direct their excess energy by placing their hands on or very close to the parts of the patient which require treatment. With a very stressed patient, the healer may place his hands on and around the patient's head. He concentrates his mind, then directs energy into the patient's brain, this type of treatment is very common. The healer uses his energy to modulate the patient's stressful High Beta brain frequencies down to the more relaxed and comfortable frequency range of Alpha.

If the spiritual healer is very skilled, he may reduce the patient's brain frequencies down to dreaming and the hypnotic frequencies of Theta. Under these circumstances, the patient's Assemblage Point can shift to a new location. Depending on the degree of shift, the patient can experience a personality change.

Theta brain wave states of consciousness (see Chapter One) can induce euphoria, pain relief, dreaming and visions. Many type of therapies, including psychotherapy and hypnotherapy, access the patient's subconscious mind by using special techniques to induce Theta states of consciousness. A person in Theta states of consciousness is very susceptible to external stimuli and suggestibility. The possibilities are enormous, not just for therapy, there are many products available which induce Theta states, such as cassette tapes to play at bedtime offering the rapid learning of foreign languages and so on.

Most schools and centres teaching meditation and other mystical disciplines do not take into account or employ Assemblage Point assessment within their curricula. Regular meditation, over a period of time, will gradually shift the Assemblage Point location from the right side of the chest across towards the centre line. It can often take years to achieve a permanent shift of a few centimetres in this way. If practiced to excess, however, the Assemblage Point will move further to the left side of the chest, accompanied by introvert states of consciousness.

Meditation methods of Assemblage Point management, generally, are only useful to achieve lateral shifts towards the left side of the chest. Despite the mountains of medical evidence that prove the benefits of meditation, medical doctors are aware of its limitations as a therapy. Meditation will not lift a dropped Assemblage Point location, such as is observed with myalgic encephalomyelitis (M.E.) or post natal depression and other serious diseases. Neither will meditation correct Assemblage Point splits and shadows, as observed in cases of schizophrenia, epilepsy and manic depression. Some schools will not teach meditation to patient with psychiatric problems unless the patient first obtains a special letter from their doctor.

Students of all types of mystical disciplines should be aware not to be lured into the common trap of the shift to the left (see Chapter One). The various altered states of consciousness and experiences, such as "bliss", "nirvana" "enlightenment", "channelling divine healing energy" and so on, which mystical disciplines can precipitate are very seductive, widely misunderstood and often misrepresented. The aspirant can easily fall prey to over evaluation of his experiences. One can easily become over propitiative and humbly grateful or even arrogant. Under these circumstances the student is extremely vulnerable to all types of propaganda, mind programming, hypnosis, suggestion and so on. Very easily, the mystical experiences can become the evidence which seems to prove the authenticity of the programme, a particular school or religion, belief system or the teacher's words. These states of consciousness are scientifically accounted for, they are completely natural, freely available to all humans and are part of our heritage. They are not the property of any particular group or method of attainment.

Another recent development is the use of the Sensory Isolation Floatation Tank for relaxation and stress reduction. This was invented by Dr. John C. Lilly back in the 1950's. The floatation tank is a temperature controlled, quiet, dark environment. Inside the tank one floats, almost gravity free, in warm high density salt water. The inputs to all of the senses, including touch, are reduced almost to zero. One is totally alone with oneself with no distraction. After some time the thinking process becomes boringly evident and it eventually stops. Other states of consciousness can manifest, including the most profound states of physical and mental relaxation and integration. Biological energy is accumulated through relaxation and suspension of Beta brain wave frequency (conscious thinking). The Assemblage Point of the average person will drift from the right side of the chest towards the centre meridian line. In his book, *The Deep Self*, Dr. Lilly states that people with mental health problems should not be allowed anywhere near a floatation tank. The floatation tank produces lateral shifts in the Assemblage Point towards the left. Dropped and split location cannot be treated in the floatation tank without expert medical supervision.

Abnormal Locations of the Assemblage Point

In the 1950's, Dr. Lilly was working with the Maryland Institute of Mental Health. He was researching the effects of L.S.D. in the floatation tank. Later he published his findings in a book, *The Centre Of The Cyclone*. At around the same period, Dr. Carlos Castaneda published *The Teachings of Don Juan*, an anthropological account of his apprenticeship to Don Juan, the American Indian shaman. The book gives explicit detailed shamanic use of hallucinogenic plants. Dr. Timothy Leary's book, *The Politics of Ecstasy* also endeavoured to explain and encourage personal experimentation with L.S.D. and other hallucinogenic drugs. Dr. Albert Hoffmann invented L.S.D. and also synthesised psilocybin, the hallucinogenic drug present in the magic mushrooms employed by native Red Indian and South American shamans and medicine men. Drs. Hoffmann, Richard Evans Schultes and Leary together with many other researchers obtained samples of the hallucinogenic plants, together with the preparation and dosage instructions from Native Indian Medicine Practitioners in remote parts of North and South America. Taking the icing but leaving behind the cake, they returned to their city offices with powerful, but incomplete, knowledge along with new tools to expand the mind.

In the late 1960's and 70's, these activities and publications were followed by an explosion of young people experimenting with hallucinogenic drugs. Hallucinogenic drugs are very powerful and they can shift the Assemblage Point to any location. They can also cause splits and shadows. Since then, there have been many casualties. Many young people have experienced personality changes and other strange symptoms. The conventional medical profession has found no answers for the problems created.

In reality, when the effect of the drug wore off, the experimenters' Assemblage Point had moved to a different location. Often, people who had been experimenting with L.S.D., would experience a phenomena called "flashbacks"; this is a temporary shift in their Assemblage Point. It shifts back to a shadow location or tunnel reality established while the user was under the effects of the drug. L.S.D. was being widely distributed, users were taking it along with alcohol and other drugs, which greatly increased the dangers, both for the users and the public. Alarm bells were ringing everywhere and the drug was made illegal.

The Two Apertures of Death

There followed books intended to add respectability together with some structure and programming for people experimenting with psychedelic drugs. For instance, Drs. Hoffman and Schultes published *Plants of the Gods: Origins of Hallucinogenic Use.* Dr. Leary and Richard Alpert produced *The Psychedelic Experience,* a modern version of W. Y. Evans Wentz's book, *The Tibetan Book of the Dead.* Later, Dr. Lilly wrote the forward for a book entitled *New American Book of the Dead. The Psychedelic Experience* was published as a guide, containing information to accompany the use of hallucinogenic drugs. The structure was taken and adapted from Tibetan and Buddhist scriptures, which encouraged meditation on the "clear light of the void" and "enlightenment". The original version by Evens-Wentz contains detailed information concerning the manipulation of an energy referred to as the "Vital Force". This Vital Force is the life force or energy that leaves the body at the moment of death. The Vital Force is manipulated by a priest, medicine man or shaman assisting the dying person. The contemporary versions of *The Tibetan Book of The Dead* promise the reader the "Holy Grail" but fail to mention the Tibetan Shamanic Death Rites and the manipulation of the dying person's Vital Force. In such manipulation, pressure is applied to arteries around the neck and at other points. These death rights are performed as the person is dying to prevent the vital energy from traversing the median nerve and exiting through the gap below the navel. The only other exit for the vital force is the crown aperture at the top of the head. The Tibetans believe that enlightenment occurs and reincarnation is prevented when the vital force passes out through the crown aperture. (If you would like to read more about this practice please refer to Evens-Wentz book *The Tibetan Book of The Dead.*) Yet again, having come so close, the Holy Grail was lost although it is obvious in the work of Evens-Wentz.

This book is loaded with descriptive details of the numerous states of consciousness and alternative realities which occur with the immanent approach of death. It also contains a maze of instructions which the person in attendance on the one dying should read out aloud in order to guide them through the process of death and navigating the ensuing realities. More importantly, it contains instructions on how, where and when to apply pressure with the fingers to the arteries of the pharynx or neck so that the person dying can retain his consciousness through the death process. It also states this is necessary for the dying person's vital life force to exit the body via the aperture at the top of the head. These death rites prevent the vital life force from returning to the cosmos via the only other aperture, which is at the umbilicus region or navel.

Human energy is finite. Regardless of the best of medicine, at the end of the day, we will all die. As yet no one has satisfactorily defined scientifically what consciousness is or its limits. The above paragraph not only discusses consciousness but relates it to the "vital force" and its importance in death. As a person approaches death, their Assemblage Point drops down towards the navel. The Assemblage Point locations of old infirm patients who are close to death, will generally always be very close to the navel line. The navel aperture is a natural hole in the human energy field that relates to the umbilical cord. For the developing foetus, the navel aperture is the source of energy and vitality, it is the source of 'great light'. This aperture is closed shortly after birth, but there remains a weak point that stays with us for life. When death occurs, the person's vital energy returns to the universe, it leaves their body by the same route that it entered in the beginning, that is, out through the navel aperture.

Prior to the death of the internationally famous guru of love and peace, Osho, he was imprisoned in Oklahoma jail. When he was released he returned to India where he died a short time later. The following notes reveal some amazing details concerning his death and the process of death. They are copied from letters written by a close friend of Osho.

". . .Interestingly, a few weeks before Osho left his body, he told me he could see the "vibrating blue light" over his forehead. He asked me to feel its powerful pulsation. He told me that if it moved over his navel it meant death. Two days later he told me it had moved to his hara or navel area. He left his body about two months later. It is felt by his medical advisors that Osho was given toxic doses of Thallium during his illegal imprisonment in Oklahoma prison."

". . .Regarding Osho, there is good reason to believe he was subjected to radioactive cobalt while he was in prison in Oklahoma jail. I guess this would do something dramatic to the assemblage point! It could have produced the magnitude of energy needed.

During the last three weeks of his life he told us he was being subjected to 'sound waves' below (or maybe above) the audible range. The rays were being used to further weaken his body. He died three weeks later. I guess that the sound frequencies could have been ELF frequencies used as a weapon. We will probably never know. What is of interest however, is that maybe ELF frequencies can be used to move the assemblage point" .

Not only in life, but even in death, it would seem that we are given a choice. *The Tibetan Book of The Dead* and many other books make it clear that there in a second aperture at the top of our head. The possibilities look exciting. We have the choice to leave the body by the normal route of the average man, that is, when our Assemblage Point traverses the navel. Or we can, by using special techniques, die another type of death, perhaps the "hero's death", with the Assemblage Point or vital force exiting through the crown aperture at the top of the head and retain full consciousness through our death process.

Dr. John Lilly maintained that enlightenment was 'an over -evaluation space'. Looking back, from the perspective of current knowledge concerning the Assemblage Point and its relationship to altered states of consciousness, birth and death, he was quite correct.

Carlos Castaneda and The Assemblage Point

Throughout this time Dr. Carlos Castaneda continued publishing books reporting on his apprenticeship with Don Juan, the shaman and medicine man. Castaneda, who held a Ph.D. in anthropology from the University of California, Los Angeles, said he met Don Juan in Arizona in the early 1960s while researching medicinal plants. He followed when the shaman moved to Sonora, Mexico. Castaneda had pushed beyond using hallucinogenic plants. In the beginning of his apprenticeship, Don Juan had used power plants to loosen Carlos Castaneda's Assemblage Point. Don Juan claimed that Castaneda's Assemblage Point was so stubbornly fixed that only hallucinogenic plants had sufficient power to shift it. In his later books, Castaneda concentrates on expounding information and details of the Assemblage Point locations and its relationship with various altered states of consciousness. In his later books, such as *The Art of Dreaming*, he seems more concerned with management of the Assemblage Point and relating states of consciousness connected with shifts in location when dreaming. Only in his book *The Fire From Within* can we find references to the medical value of the Assemblage Point. Although Castaneda recorded Don Juan's references concerning the medical dangers of abnormal Assemblage Point locations, unfortunately it seems that he failed to enquire for more details. Or perhaps Don Juan gave more details about the dangers to health than Castaneda has related to his readers. In this book, Castaneda records Don Juan's talking about the Assemblage point. Don Juan is reported as saying that a situation which is particularly dangerous is an involuntary shift of the Assemblage Point due to physical fatigue, emotional or physical exhaustion, disease. On another occasion in this book, Don Juan is reported as saying that people who unwittingly shift their Assemblage Point by taking drugs, can induce a feeling of numbness and cold and have difficulty in talking and thinking; as if they were frozen from inside. Don Juan also spoke extensively about the process of death and the gap at the navel.

It is very clear that the character, Don Juan, held important medical knowledge concerning the location of the Assemblage Point and health. Castaneda's books are riddled with such dire warnings from the master, Don Juan. It is very clear that Don Juan knew what he was talking about, but Castaneda shrouded and embellished the master's conversations in a literary mystique. At no point throughout any of Castaneda's books, does he indicate to his reader how a dropped or misaligned Assemblage Point should be corrected.

There are many authoritative people who consider Castaneda to be a hoaxer. The fact is that there is an obvious truth in the words of Don Juan's knowledge of the Assemblage Point, as Castaneda reported them. However, there is now considerable evidence, especially with respect to his seminars, training workshops and most recent publications, that he has either not fully understood Don Juan's teachings concerning the Assemblage Point, or perhaps he may have deliberately misrepresented them. The following is a quotation from a letter received in connection with this subject:

"I have been practising these "Magical Passes" for three years. It may take years for one to move one's own Assemblage Point by these movements . . . .. Now you are saying that moving the Assemblage Point is a quick and simple manoeuvre. Now who do I believe here? You maintain that the energy body is around us already. Castaneda maintains that the energy body is very far away, that it has been driven away by forces unknown to man since early childhood or perhaps shortly after being born. I tend to think that our energy body is always with us until we die. Castaneda maintains that the Assemblage Point is at the rear, at arms' length from the back."

When Castaneda wrote *Magical Passes*, he must have forgotten what he wrote about shifting the Assemblage Point in his earlier book, *The Fire From Within*. In the latter he describes how Don Juan regularly shifted his Assemblage Point by an unexpected blow to his right shoulder blade. Castaneda's Assemblage Point was habitually on the right side of his chest. The description of the Assemblage Point as presented by his quotations from Don Juan's actual words in *The Fire From Within* calls into question the validity of his later works to the serious student of the Assemblage Point.

Left And Right Brain Realities

In the meantime, Dr. Leary and Robert Anton Wilson developed and published maps and models of human consciousness based on established brain research studies and its results.

According to Anton Wilson's model of consciousness, in his book *Prometheus Rising*, the left brain lobe has completely different mental functions to that of the right brain. Today his model has been widely accepted and it is in daily use by many informed and even more not so well informed individuals. One regularly hears statements from individuals such as: "I am a right brain person, a dreamer and I'm artistic" or "I'm a left brain person and I'm logical and clever"! These beliefs were acquired from the results and publications of brain researchers in the fifties and sixties who monitored the brain wave frequencies and activities in each half of the brain of volunteers participating and performing different types of mental and physical tasks, including sleeping and dreaming.

The researchers used an electronic recording instrument called an electroencephalogram or EEG machine to monitor the subjects' brainwave activities and frequencies. The electroencephalogram is connected to numerous points around the skull with electrodes. These electrodes are connected to the recorder by wires in much the same way as a doctor's electrocardiogram or ECG monitor used to monitor the electrical signals of the heart.

These researchers established that when performing mental tasks, such as mathematics, sitting examinations or worrying, the left brain was very much more active than the right brain and the brain frequencies were much higher than when the subject was relaxed. Conversely, they established that when a subject was engaged in activities such as art or music the right brain was more active and the frequencies were much slower. In sleep they established that the frequencies were very slow and, when dreaming, the frequencies were midway between sleep and being relaxed.

The liver is on the right side of the body, which is controlled by the left side of the brain. The spleen is on the left side of the body which is controlled by the right side of the brain.

Stressful experiences, such as sitting exams, require very high liver activity to meet the brain/body demands for glucose and other substances which are required to maintain attention, tension, brain activity and muscle tension. Such experiences have a dry characteristic, that is, the mouth can become dry. The spleen is part of the lymphatic system and artistic and musical activities for example are emotional and have a wet characteristic, that is, the eyes can become tearful.

Taking it a step further, when one considers that at night time, as we fall asleep, the brain and body do not require so much glucose and the liver shuts down, it also drops in temperature (see Appendix VI). At the same time the left brain temperature drops and the right brain and the spleen temperatures increase. It could be argued that these early researches were not measuring the brain's "thinking" or "dreaming" signals at all. It is more than likely that what they were actually recording was the brain's signalling messages to these two large organs and other body components. If this is true, the question of where thinking takes place in the brain has yet to be established. This possibility is compounded by all of the reports from patients in comma and whilst under the influences of anaesthetics where very little brain activity can be recorded..

According to the Anton Wilson's model, the left brain is divided into four separate hardware circuits and these circuits are associated with four distinct states of consciousness that he claims coincided with four distinct stages of prehistoric human evolution of the brain. The model is difficult to take on board as it would seem from it that prehistoric man, shortly after he evolved from apes only had half a brain - the left lobe. And it was not until more recently in man's evolution that the other half developed - the right lobe. Despite this, his model is very interesting and is quite useful for some individuals as a learning tool and it gives his readers a map of the territory of higher domains of consciousness and man's possibilities for further mental and spiritual development. Anton Wilson divides the brain's hardware and respective functions as follows:

The Four Left Brain Lobe Circuits

1. At birth the first circuit is active and is obsessed with biological survival and is fixated on sucking and feeding along with physical security. In

adults, sleeping pills, morphine and heroin will attenuate all of the following circuits and thus activate this circuit.

2. The second circuit is activated at around two to three years of age. It is preoccupied with territory and the power struggles within the family structure. Here the child learns the processes associated with the rituals of submission and domination. It has to learn the rules of the tribal emotional games and its place within the group. In adults, this circuit is activated by alcohol as it attenuates the higher brain functions.

3. The third circuit comes into action when the child is between five and seven years old. It is programmed and conditioned by man-made objects and graphical symbol systems. It adapts and manages and categorises the environment, separating and sorting everything according to society's beliefs. It is also a means of transporting the artifacts and symbols from history into the future. Caffeine, amphetamines and cocaine amplify this circuit.

4. The fourth circuit in the left lobe is programmed at puberty by the first orgasm or mating experience. Its programme limitations are defined by society's attitudes and belief about sex. It adapts to society's definition of what is allowed and what is forbidden with regard to procreation and mating. It is preoccupied with relationships, culture, politics, social welfare and economics. Sexual hormones are the activators of this circuit.

The Four Right Brain Lobe Circuits

According to Anton Wilson, this second group of four brain circuits are only operating in a small percentage of individuals and these percentages decrease with each circuit increment.

5. In order for the fifth circuit to become activated and functional, the individual has to be initiated by a holistic approach and practice special physical and mental disciplines, which often include special diets. Anton Wilson calls this the "Holistic Neurosamatic Circuit" and it is programmed by ecstatic experiences acquired by following disciplines such as meditation, yoga, chanting, praying, isolation, faith healing and so on. It is differentiated from the left brain circuits by ecstatic feelings of bliss and physical rapture. The drug cannabis and Tantric yoga practices are specific methods of activating this circuit.

6. The sixth circuit is the residing place of Jung's archetypal collective consciousness. Here one can discover Cherubs, Seraphims, Gods and Goddesses, Demons, Kali, Dwarfs, Elves, Fairies and all of the other disincarnate entities of mythology. This circuit is activated by advanced Tantric and Kundalini yogas, peyote, mescaline, psilocybin and methylated amphetamines.

7. Anton Wilson's seventh heaven circuit is activated and programmed by very advanced yogas and mystical disciplines. In this circuit, logic can transcend itself by itself and reprogramme and restructure the foregoing six circuits below. It can reprogramme itself by itself to infinity making possible a myriad of choices between an infinite number of different windows of reality. L.S.D. and Ketamine are the specific chemicals that activate this circuit.

8. "Up through the seventh gate and into circuit eight I rose." Circuit eight is activated and programmed by shock, or by near death or clinical death experiences. Anton Wilson calls this circuit "The Non-Local Quantum Circuit" This is the quantum of consciousness and out of body experiences (see Appendix VI). Here one apparently finds oneself outside the physical body, outside of the confines of time and in some other universe. At this level one is almost pure essence and is not restricted by time or distance and is not limited to the speed of light. Anaesthetics can activate this circuit.

To some extent this map or model fits in with what we now understand about the different locations of the Assemblage Point and the related states of consciousness. The left brain circuits two and three correspond with various Assemblage Point locations on the right side of the chest. Right brain circuits six, seven and eight correspond to locations on the left side. With circuits four and five, the location is around the centre of the chest. And circuit one can be found very low down near the navel.

However, whether these circuits exist in the left and right brain lobes is highly questionable. As already pointed out above and in chapter one, left and right brain activity has probably more to do with the way the liver and spleen are functioning, which controls the operating state of consciousness. This in turn is mirrored by the location of the Assemblage Point which dictates how we feel and how we behave. With depression and M.E. the Assemblage Point is low and the patient has no energy and energy is a function of the liver. Anton Wilson's model only makes sense if there is only one functioning Assemblage Point location.

When two Assemblage Point locations come into play (causing schizophrenia), the territory is much more complicated, unpredictable and also dangerous. Certain schizophrenic states habitually locate in or switch between Assemblage Point locations corresponding to circuits two and six. Anton Wilson floundered badly in his book while trying to present an adequate explanation or models to explain oscillating and bipolar states of consciousness. However, having raised the subject, he promptly dismissed it by stating that negative neurosomatic circuits are experienced by some cannabis users, amateur yogis and schizophrenics. When a person's biological energy levels are increased beyond a certain threshold, by whatever means, and if their Assemblage Point is badly positioned, they will almost certainly experience a negative crisis. Forced confinement and social isolation, mystical disciplines, drugs and fanatical behaviour can induce powerful emotional disturbances by increasing biological energy to a critical level. Sufferers of negative neurosomatic states of consciousness, and all people close to them, are desperate for a solution to the vexing problems that can arise from such states of consciousness.

Case 7. Chronic Mental Illness with Depression.

Ian B, aged 28. 13 November 1996. Ian was referred via London doctors for assessment and treatment. His situation had become so untenable that he was going to be hospitalised for further psychiatric drug therapy. This sensitive young man presented with a grey complexion, very low biological energy and seriously depressed frontal brain energy. His brain frequency rhythms were predominantly in the theta band (3.3-7 Hz = dreaming/trance states). His mother reported that he was experiencing aggressive, violent, and destructive outbursts, but most of the time was totally depressed. He had periodically vandalised his home, and had thrown furniture, smashing the living room window. Examination revealed that his stationary Assemblage Point was located only 6 cm above the critical line (navel); also, the rear location or pivot point was below the shoulder blades, which nearly always has a detrimental affect on muscular co-ordination. He also had a number of shadow locations. At some time in the past, possibly when he had become ill in Germany, or perhaps due to the numerous depressive drugs including chlorpromazine, prescribed by his psychiatrist, Ian's Assemblage Point had dropped to this dangerous location. This would have caused him extreme physical and emotional distress and would have been responsible for his symptoms. Hunched posture, low frontal brain energy and lack of alpha and beta electrical brain-wave activity, as in this case, are synonymous with low locations of the Assemblage Point.

Ian's Assemblage Point was manually shifted up and across to the centre of his chest (thymus area), a total distance of some 30 cm. His frontal brain was stimulated and energised at Beta (alertness) brain-wave frequencies, using electronic gem therapy lamps. At the same time, his temporal lobes were treated. After treatment, Ian's mother said that he had not looked so well in years. Ian was instructed to return within 14 days, for further correction and treatment.

On Ian's second visit (25 November 1996), his Assemblage Point had dropped somewhat. This was to be expected after such a long illness. His frontal lobe and throat area were low in energy, but less so than at his previous visit. His complexion and posture remained substantially improved. He was more talkative, friendly and extrovert. His mother reported that he had been singing and playing his cello. Ian received similar treatment to that on his first visit and his Assemblage Point was shifted to a central position again.

On his third visit (9 December 1996), it was clear that Ian's condition had continued to improve. His Assemblage Point location had stabilised, slightly to the right of centre (normal). He was physically and mentally much stronger. His mother said that he had attended an orchestral rehearsal at a local college, playing his cello. His treatment was adjusted, taking into account his improved situation.

The Nuisance of Tunnel Realities

In these times, many people have access to two or more different tunnel realities or modes of perceiving the world around them. Such people will have two or more different patterns of behaviour. This is easy to understand. In the case where a child is brought up with one set of parents, and a divorce creates a second set, the child will have two locations of parental reference. If the new situation is vastly different from the first, the child's Assemblage Point will shift accordingly. This child now has the choice of two possible locations, two ways of perceiving the world and two modes of behaviour. This is not an efficient or comfortable situation: anytime within the person's lifetime, re-stimulation by circumstances can trigger a shift or switch from one of the childhood's Assemblage Point locations to the other. When this happens, the person is unconscious of the shift in his Assemblage Point. The circumstances that caused the re-stimulation get the blame. The truth is never uncovered, but the people involved usually believe the shift to be purely mental. It is not mental, but the result of a shift in the location of the Assemblage Point.

The above case stands in contrast to that of a child brought up in a well-balanced and stable home and educational environment. Such children usually grow up with a stable personality, enjoy good health, have many friends, and are generally successful in life. Such persons are fortunate in having a stable Assemblage Point location.

In modern times, involuntary shifts and abnormal Assemblage Point locations are a major source of unhappiness, poor physical and mental health and unsatisfactory life conditions and achievements.

Case 8. Concussion-related Social and Alcohol Problems

Mr David H, aged 32. October 1994. This strong, hard-working man complained of feeling different from other people. He wanted to know why others avoided his company. He was drinking too much and felt dejected; his behaviour was unpredictable and this was getting him into trouble with the police. He also thought others were afraid of him. He further added that his troubles had started some years back, after someone gave him a bang on his head with a lump of wood.

David's Assemblage Point alignment was abnormally different to that of the average person, probably due to his head injury. We pointed this out to him and realigned his Assemblage Point to the centre of his chest. This was a turning point for him. As the months passed, his behaviour became more socially acceptable, suggesting that the misalignment had been responsible for his antisocial behaviour. He had been projecting his feelings of paranoia onto external situations, thus triggering incidents that involved him with the police.

Violence, drunkenness, drug and substance addiction and abuse, crime and other antisocial behaviour are all associated with extreme Assemblage Point locations. People involved in these activities are generally not connected to consensus social realities. If they seem connected, it is because they switch back and forth between different Assemblage Point locations. Many people spend unnecessary time in hospitals, mental institutions and prisons on the account of the splits, shadows and variations in their Assemblage Point location. Mental institutions and prisons are notoriously ineffective at rehabilitation. Generally, old locations are suppressed with drugs or by other means. Often a third Assemblage Point location or tunnel reality is acquired whilst in prison. When these institutions start to address the core of the problem, which is misalignment of the Assemblage Point, the tax payer can be saved enormous sums of money. The patients and inmates can also be spared the indignity of long-term confinement and can receive real rehabilitation and learning. Hopefully this book will find its way into the prison libraries and some inmates will be able to help themselves.

In less extreme cases, victims of Assemblage Point misalignment spend fortunes on therapies trying to gain an insight and understanding into the nature of their problems. The success of doctors, psychiatrists, psychologists and alternative and complementary therapists is dependent on the degree of the misalignment of their patient's Assemblage Point and the number of shadows and splits involved. Since neither the patient nor the doctor is aware of the real problem, success is limited, with drug support and anaesthetising the symptoms being the only current option.

The Urgency for Assemblage Point Therapy

In the United Kingdom, patients suffering from clinical depression are often referred for electro convulsive shock therapy (E.C.T.). This therapy was introduced by the post-war psychiatric profession, in an attempt to help discharged military personnel suffering from shell shock and combat related depressive illness. The patient's brain is given an electric shock across the temples. Two electrodes are attached, one to each side of the head, and a relatively high voltage is applied to the patient. Sometimes the electro convulsive shock therapy is effective in shifting the Assemblage Point up, but often it causes more damage. The famous war correspondent and author Ernest Hemingway underwent electro convulsive shock therapy before his suicide. Probably, in his case, electro convulsive shock therapy shifted his Assemblage Point to an even more intolerable location. The following case illustrates the uselessness of electro convulsive shock therapy. However, at least the patient's prognosis and fate was better than that of Hemingway.

Case 9. Clinical Depression

Jane W., aged 46. November 1997. Jane had been suffering from clinical depression for the past 10 years. Over the years, her consultants had prescribed drugs, electro convulsive shock therapy, and long-term counselling. She had a variety of symptoms. Her current medication was a cocktail of four different drugs. Her Assemblage Point was found to be low on the right side of the body, entering at an acute angle through her liver area (typical M.E. location). Jane received three corrections to the alignment of her Assemblage Point over a 6 week period. After her second treatment, she was able to return to driving her car.

Electro convulsive shock therapy is unreliable, barbaric and downright unscientific. Before the doctors introduced a general anaesthetic into the therapy procedure, patients sometimes experienced convulsions so strong that their bones would break. No doubt patients also experienced "enlightenment" and "the clear light of the void" as their brain cooked when the amps struck. Thankfully, today the situation is gradually improving. Currently the numbers of medical doctors and therapists employing Assemblage Point locations within their diagnosis and treatment procedures are on the increase. These practitioners are achieving astounding results and success rates and saving orthodox health services small fortunes. The following cases exemplify the financial, ethical and compassionate necessity for Assemblage Point diagnosis and correction therapy to be made standard procedure in orthodox medical practice.

Case 10. Periodic Dislocation of the Hip

Veronica S., aged 16. May 1998. This young lady complained of headaches, lower back pain and a painful left knee. Her main problem was that her right hip joint would periodically dislocate, although she was tall with a sporting body tone. She was scheduled for hip surgery. Veronica was requested to walk slowly back and forth across the room; members of her family were present, and everyone observed that her frame was twisted towards her right side from the hips upwards. Her Assemblage Point was located on the left side of the chest meridian, entering at an acute angle. Left locations are not common. After her Assemblage Point was corrected she was left to relax for 20 minutes. As she walked back and forth across the room once more, all present could see that her frame was now aligned properly. On her second visit, 2 weeks later, she reported that her headaches, knee, and back pain had cleared up. Her parents cancelled the hip surgery. Prior to puberty, Veronica had had dyslexia problems. There is some evidence to suggest that dyslexia is associated with pre-puberty Assemblage Point locations on the left side of the chest. This would induce low left brain and high right brain energy at the wrong time of educational development of child.

There is now evidence that it is possible to treat dyslexia by correcting the

Assemblage Point or by energy medicine to the left brain. Dyslexia could be a mild form of autism which may also indicate low left brain activity associated with left side Assemblage Point locations. The current medical opinion that dyslexia is caused by genetic inheritance is no solution to the problem. It is a convenient and expensive research excuse for medical deficiency to find a solution for an apparently genetic disease. This subject is considered in more depth in Chapter Seven.

Case 11. Continual Cold, Trauma, Migraines and Lack of Energy

Gladys H., aged 50. May 1998. This introvert rational lady had been ill for 10 months with a continual cold, trauma, migraines, lack of energy and inability to work. Her Assemblage Point location was entering upwards from low down around her liver area. Gladys received Assemblage Point correction and electronic gem therapy. On her second visit she reported that she felt 100% better, with more energy, sleeping through the night, dreaming more, and much happier. Her cold and sinus problems had cleared up.

Case 12. Stress, Anxiety, Nervous Panic, Irritable Bowel Syndrome and Diarrhoea

Karen N., retired. February 1998. This introvert lady was presenting stress, anxiety, nervous panic, irritable bowel syndrome, and diarrhoea. She had developed these symptoms since the death of her mother. She was taking tranquillisers, and various homeopathic remedies. Her Assemblage Point was located high on the right side, entering at an acute angle from the left. Over the months she received several corrections to her Assemblage Point and made a slow, steady recovery. After the first correction, her anxiousness diminished and she was able to view her health more rationally.

Case 13. Myalgic encephalomyelitis (M.E.)

Ms Grace R, aged 26, October 1995. This educated introvert lady with a rational disposition had been suffering from ME for a number of years. She complained that her general health had been gradually deteriorating, which presented as chronic tiredness, excessive menstruation, bleeding gums, sore throat and constipation. Grace told us that she was vegetarian, that she had stopped taking her doctor's prescribed medications, and that she had tried various other therapies. veering off to the right. Her Assemblage Point had to be corrected. Her throat area was calmed with emerald and sapphire gem therapy. This included a profound 30 minute relaxation therapy, using diamond and blue sapphire to her head at a brain wave frequency Theta (3.3 Hz). This single treatment was her "turning point", shortly after which Grace took up T'ai Chi lessons. She made a full recovery in less than a year.

Case 14. Depression and Eczema following Bereavement

Mrs A. B., retired. April 1996. This lady had developed eczema with very irritating symptoms 18 months earlier, following the sudden death of two close relatives. She was taking sleeping pills, antihistamine tablets and hydrocortisone ointment. More recently, her skin was showing abnormal discoloured patches. The hospital had suggested that it might be skin cancer and that she required tests. She was hot and itching all over her body and was also anxious, nervous and angry. On examination, her Assemblage Point was below her right breast and aligned downwards to the right side.

Her Assemblage Point was corrected and she received electronic gem therapy using emerald and blue sapphire gems, with a green filter. The lamps were set at a slow, relaxing Theta frequency and were directed at the crown of her head to interrupt the itching sensations. As treatment went on, the itching and redness subsided. Mrs A.B. required two further treatments, after which she was able to discontinue her medications and her husband was reportedly "absolutely delighted".

Logically, nobody wants to be in the situation where they or someone close to them experiences an involuntary shift of their Assemblage Point. Everyone would like to maintain a stable location and the benefits of a long term stable personality and behaviour patterns, along with lifestyles that go with this. However, logic and rational thought cannot control the Assemblage Point.

At any moment life can deliver such a hard blow that, even among the healthiest and most rational of us, the blow is sufficient to dislodge our Assemblage Point. For these reasons and all that has been mentioned above, it is necessary to have some economical, effective and repeatable methods of locating and correcting the human Assemblage Point. It is absolutely essential that the medical profession employ Assemblage Point assessment and diagnosis for their patients. In the near future, vast sums of money and human suffering will be saved as Assemblage point science becomes recognised and utilised throughout educational, health and social services.

chapter 3

THE HAZARDS OF DRUGS, TOXINS, POISONS, POLLUTION AND BRAINWASHING

There are many drugs and other common hazards which shift the Assemblage Point location. It is necessary to take these into consideration in order to gain an overview of the relationship between the Assemblage Point location and health. Many people and those close to them have had their lives ruined by the consumption of drugs or exposure to toxins, poisons, pollution or brain washing.

Most of us know of someone who is a victim of contact or exposure to these hazards. The uninformed, the poor, the socially deprived and people suffering with poor health are most at risk and least able to help themselves. Today, there is a prolific supply of all types of drugs and many of them are all too easily available. For the rest of us, the risks of accidental contact with thousands of different obnoxious chemicals, poisons, toxins and pollution is very high.

Understanding how these hazards affect and manipulate our Assemblage Points is absolutely essential in today's modern world. Anyone who is suffering as a result of contact with these hazards will find the information below most helpful. Assemblage Point correction will provide a path back to health and freedom.

Although not essential, for the clinical application of Assemblage Point diagnosis and correction therapy, a background knowledge of the effects of drugs and other hazards, including a general psychological background can be helpful. Patients who are chronically ill will benefit from additional supportive medication or therapy. What is presented below is the best data available at the time of printing. It should not be considered to be conclusive and is open to correction, improvement and further research by other investigators.

Concerning the effect of drugs on the Assemblage Point location, the same drug will affect individual people in different ways. A number of factors determine the way a person will react to a specific drug. Some of these factors are the body weight, constitution, physiological structure, and psychological type, general health, diet and the age of the person. Another critical factor is the location of the person's Assemblage Point.

For example, introvert nervous persons, with a thin frame, prone to anxiety and panic, will have a corresponding Assemblage Point location. It will be rather high and on the right side of the chest, as in figure 3.1.

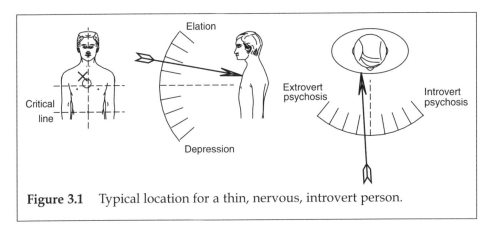

Figure 3.1   Typical location for a thin, nervous, introvert person.

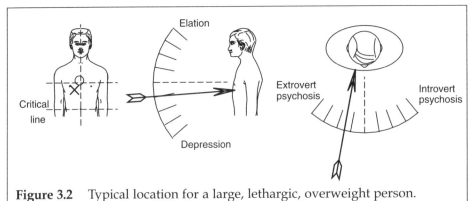

Figure 3.2   Typical location for a large, lethargic, overweight person.

These types of people, who tend to be very physically active, will be inclined towards herbal teas, alcohol, tranquillisers and sleeping pills. These have the effect of slowing down their nervous system. Stimulants such as amphetamines, cocaine or hallucinogenic drugs and certain types of cannabis preparations can be very dangerous for introvert sensitive persons with this Assemblage Point location.

In contrast, broad framed, extrovert persons, prone to lethargy and overweight, will have a lower Assemblage Point location, as depicted in figure 3.2. These types will be inclined towards stimulating drugs, such as coffee, amphetamines or cocaine. Tranquillisers, sleeping pills or cannabis, will generally not suit persons with a low Assemblage Point location, as they will make this type even more lethargic and depressed.

There is no medical drug known to the author which can raise and centralise the Assemblage Point from a dropped location. Medical placebos and blind and randomised controlled clinical trials, as yet, do not consider the patient's energy field or Assemblage Point location in their preliminary diagnosis procedures. Without this information, the results of such trials are based on insufficient patient assessment, and, therefore, the value of the results and data gained is questionable. The reason for this is that recovery from disease or symptoms caused or associated with low locations is very difficult or impossible without correcting the Assemblage Point of the patient. This problem gets worse with age. This would adversely affect the results of medical trials, as those patients with low locations would not respond well. The location of the patient's Assemblage Point can adversely affect the results of trials. Two examples are given later in this chapter with reference to the effects of mercury on M.E..

The Assemblage Point location is the key to correct diagnosis of the patient's current state of health, consciousness and vibrational rate. Monitoring and mapping the Stationary Assemblage Point is useful in helping the clinician to decide the type of drug and the dosage that would improve their patient's Assemblage Point location. Adopting Assemblage Point mapping would substantially reduce the risk for the patient of experiencing a negative or allergic reaction.

Prescribed Drugs

Central nervous system depressants, such as morphine, heroin, chlorpromazine, lithium salts, lorazepam, barbiturates etc., can drive the Stationary Assemblage Point downwards. These types of drugs suppress the electrical activity in the nervous system, therefore the patient's vibrational rate is much slower and, correspondingly, the Assemblage Point location will move to a lower location to reflect this. When the Assemblage Point is close to the critical line, the use of central nervous system depressants (and general anaesthetics) is very dangerous, as they can drive the Assemblage Point down past the critical line. With low locations, the patient's biological energy levels are depleted and death could result. Many frail patients have died whilst receiving minor surgery under general anaesthetics. Often, in such circumstances, the patient is transferred to a life support system. After a respectable period of time, the relatives are informed that the patient had an allergic reaction to the general anaesthetic. For frail patients with a low Assemblage Point location scheduled for minor surgical procedures, it is safer to administer local or dis-associating anaesthetics such as benzocaine or its analogies or ketamine hydrochloride.

Case 15. Dropped Assemblage Point due to Drug Overdose

Mr. David R., aged 62. 1987. This very intelligent and kind man was receiving medication for sleeping problems and severe stress. The emergency services were called to his home in the early hours of the morning. His apartment was flooded and David was discovered unconscious in a cold bath with the taps running. He was taken to hospital and released the following evening. He telephoned in a distraught state, saying that something was very wrong with him, but he did not know what it was.

On examination the following day, his Assemblage Point was located only 9 cm above his navel. He had very little physical or mental energy. His other symptoms were intense burning and discomfort in his bladder; he would have to visit the bathroom every few minutes. His respiration was very laboured.

His Assemblage Point was shifted vertically upwards and across slightly to using electronic gem therapy. Both treatments were completely successful and he was back at his desk the following day.

Withdrawal from central nervous system depressant drugs will cause the electrical activity of the nervous system to increase dramatically. Therefore, the patient's Assemblage Point will move to a high location and entry angle. This will be accompanied with excessive frontal brain energy and High Beta frequency activity and may in turn lead to anxiety, panic, manic or psychotic type symptoms, as well physical symptoms such as gastro-intestinal disturbances. The problem of addiction is in part due to the fact that the body changes the way it functions to compensate for the presence of the depressive drug. If a person has been taking depressive drugs for a long period, then the body's compensating mechanisms may take many months to return to normal. Shifting the patient's Assemblage Point will be of substantial assistance in the withdrawal process.

As outlined in the previous chapters, Assemblage Point locations on the right are inherently unstable. Manic depression, which is a called a "bipolar disorder", has a right side Assemblage Point location. The sufferer oscillates between an elevated entry angle when in the manic phase and a low entry angle when in the depressed mode. However, the Assemblage Points rear location pivot point remains around the same location in both phases. The oscillations of the Assemblage Point angle can be stabilised with drugs such as lithium salts. However, shifting the Assemblage Point to the centre will stabilise the patient's condition.

Schizophrenia is a much more serious problem, as it involves the oscillation of the Assemblage Point between two or more locations. Unlike manic depression, the schizophrenic patient's pivotal point moves between locations.

Even more serious is epilepsy and in some cases the Assemblage Point can move very close to the critical line. Petty mal and grand mal seizures seem to restore the Assemblage Point to a higher location. This can be either on the left or the right side of the chest, depending on the patient's health and predilection. If the seizure restores the Assemblage Point to a location high on the right, the patient can lead a normal life between fits. The location to which the Assemblage Point is restored after the seizure will be accompanied with the symptoms associated with the location. Shifting the Assemblage Point location close to the centre will help to re-balance the patient's endocrine system. Therefore the seizures may be less frequent. Pathological Assemblage Point locations will increase the frequency of seizures.

Keeping a daily record of the patient's Assemblage Point location will give an indication when a change of their condition is going to occur. For example, in the case of epilepsy, this would indicate when a fit is about to commence. Shifting the Assemblage Point back up manually may help to prevent the onset of a fit. All serious mental health disorders are associated with Assemblage Point locations in extreme positions to the right or left side.

Encouraging patients to maintain a central Assemblage Point location will greatly reduce their symptoms and their medication requirements. Patients who are taking drugs for depression, anxiety and other disorders such as diabetes, will generally require a complete re-evaluation of their medication after their Assemblage Point is corrected to the centre location.

Central nervous system stimulants such as cocaine, amphetamines and antidepressants drive the Assemblage Point to the right and upwards. However, their ability to raise the Assemblage Point up from a low position, the M.E. location, for example, is not effective due to the stress which they impart on the already depleted biological energy. Central nervous system stimulants can induce psychotic symptoms if the Assemblage Point is in a high location. Shifting the stationary Assemblage Point to the centre will alleviate drug withdrawal symptoms and significantly speed up rehabilitation.

Case 16. Ecstasy, Cocaine and Amphetamine Misuse

Ms K.J., aged 22. February 1997. This extrovert young lady had been using ecstasy, cocaine and amphetamines some 3 years previously. She had recently been experiencing panic attacks and pain in her ears, the latter thought by her doctor to be caused by an infection. Her Assemblage Point was found to be far to the right and entering from a very acute angle on her right side. Some 10 minutes after her Assemblage Point was corrected, she experienced a "popping" sensation in each ear. Kate's anxiety cleared up with a single correction.

Case 17. Circulation Problems with Heart Palpitations

Ms E.G., aged 24. March 1998. This young lady had previously been taking amphetamines ("speed") with some friends. Since then, she had been experiencing hot flushes, numb fingers, hands and feet, circulation problems and heart palpitations. Her Assemblage Point location, as expected, was entering at an acute angle on the far right and from the right passing through her heart. Her symptoms cleared after correction. Her pulse was checked before and after correction. Prior to the shift, her pulse was fast, irregular and jerky. Correction changed it to a slower, steady and strong beat, her hot flushes and circulation symptoms cleared up.

Chemotherapy drugs deplete biological energy very rapidly. These drugs are designed to kill cancer cells and not normal cells, therefore these drugs are toxic. As cancer and A.I.D.S. patients are biologically depressed and probably traumatised, they will almost certainly have low Assemblage Point locations. There is evidence to indicate that chemotherapy drugs may compound the patient's situation by driving the Assemblage Point even lower. Long term Assemblage Point misalignment may be partly or wholly responsible for the conditions leading to cancer and A.I.D.S.. Shifting the Assemblage Point up to a central position gives the patient renewed energy and perspective and may prove to be a major benefit therapeutically, by correcting and balancing the functions of the organs and endocrine glands.

There is some good news here. If cancerous cells can be killed off by toxic drugs or controlled exposure to X-rays (radiation therapy) and normal cells are only weakened by such treatments, then cancerous cells are actually weaker than normal cells. To design effective treatments using energy medicine, consideration should be given to increase the biological energy of the blood, organs and glands of the patient and reduce the biological energy of the cancerous cells. One literally needs to take away the libido of cancerous cells and increase the resilience of the healthy cells. Energy medicine treatments for several types of cancer are discussed in Chapter Seven.

Tobacco

Normally, smoking tobacco has very little or no effect on the Assemblage Point location. If it does anything, it increases the heart rate and tends to bend the Assemblage Point towards the right side. There are many millions of people who enjoy, regret and repent of smoking and their Assemblage Point locations are generally normal and typical. For some people with an Assemblage Point location high on the right, tobacco can trigger heart palpitations and induce feelings of anxiety, panic and feelings of losing control.

Alcohol

Alcohol causes a small misalignment or bending of the Stationary Assemblage Point to the right side and downwards. Excessive consumption causes gross misalignment to the right and can induce psychotic behaviour. Addiction can occur if the Assemblage Point is seriously misaligned, as in figure 3.3. Without alcohol, and the same applies for depressive drugs, the patient feels bad and drinks or takes drugs to reduce the body's electrical activity and accompanying Beta brain frequency activity and related physical symptoms. The violent and destructive behaviour of some alcoholics is partly due to their Assemblage Point location, which is on the extreme right, the location for extrovert psychosis. As younger males, in general, have an Assemblage Point location on the right side; the consumption of large quantities of alcohol in a short period of time dramatically increases the likelihood of violent behaviour.

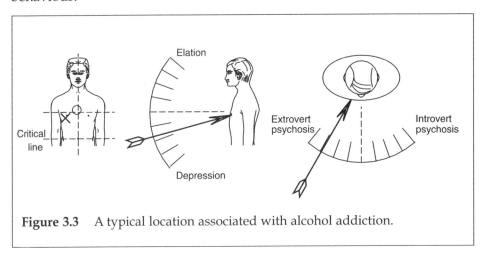

Figure 3.3   A typical location associated with alcohol addiction.

Alcohol when consumed along with other drugs is dangerous. Alcohol when combined with central nervous system depressive drugs such as barbiturates, will induce narcosis and can be fatal. This combination will cause the Assemblage Point to drop rapidly.

When alcohol is combined with anti-depressive drugs, the outcome is dangerously unpredictable. In this case, the stimulating effects of antidepressant drugs combined with the intoxicating effects of alcohol can result in psychotic episodes. The Assemblage Point moves to the right and is high.

Accompanying the dramatic increase in the consumption of prescribed anti-depressive drugs, in the last few years there have been a number of tragic homicides. Alcohol combined with depressive drugs is one of the methods of committing suicide, death is self inflicted. But in cases where alcohol has been consumed with antidepressants, causing a psychotic episode, death has been inflicted on other members of their family.

A person with suicidal tendencies will have a low Assemblage Point location. Correcting the Assemblage Point location will change their mood and make them feel much better within themselves. People who depend on antidepressants in order to feel good can reduce the risks, save themselves money and improve their health by getting their Assemblage Point shifted to the centre. The central location produces a natural feeling of well being and from this location life's problems can be fun; one does not need to escape with drugs.

Case 18. Depression and Drug and Alcohol Dependence

Ms J. S., aged 25. November 1993. This pretty, intelligent and sensitive young lady was 7 months pregnant. For a number of years previously, she had been taking numerous prescribed and illegal drugs, mainly strong central nervous system depressants. At times, she would also take illegal stimulants. On top of this, she had a problem with alcohol. She had been hospitalised several times, suffering from drug psychoses. J.S. had managed to reduce her intake of drugs and drink over the months of her pregnancy. However, this did nothing to improve the way she felt inside.

J.S. had been persuaded to attend a local self-help support group, where members met to talk and share their experiences. There were a number of people present with diagnosed psychological problems. At this meeting, her Assemblage Point was centralised and raised from a low position beneath her right breast. At the next meeting 2 weeks later, she told the group that she now felt in control of her life again. She had more physical energy and was able to get on with things that previously had been too much effort. She said that the effects of the Assemblage Point shift were very pronounced for the first 5 days. Her Assemblage Point had slipped to the right and down a little since the previous correction. This was put right again. At a follow-up appointment 2 years later, both J.S. and her baby boy were healthy and happy.

Shifting the Assemblage Point to the centre can greatly help rehabilitation, as it will reduce the patient's symptoms. The irony of alcohol is that it can give relief for the arising symptoms of Assemblage Point locations on the right, but in doing so it causes the Assemblage Point to drift even further to the right. This is the alcohol trap exposed. When the Assemblage Point is in the central location, the consumption of alcohol is not required to suppress symptoms. It can be enjoyed normally as there is no compulsion to consume it. In addition, it does not have as much effect and it can be quite difficult to feel "drunk" from the central location.

Cannabis

Some types of cannabis preparations, such as dark resin, reduce Beta brain frequencies to Alpha and Theta, which reduces the user's "internal dialogue". The effects, at least for some people, are said to increase left and right brain synergy. Unlike alcoholics, cannabis users usually display an agreeable nature and their Assemblage Point will be closer to the centre meridian line. Many users claim to be more in touch with their feelings when using the various preparations of this plant.

For the habitual consumers, problems arise when the drug is unavailable because the central nervous system adapts to the influence of cannabis in the body. Withdrawal sends the Assemblage Point to the right and upwards and induces High Beta frequency activity in the brain, with accompanying distressing symptoms. Cannabis users often resort to alcohol or other substitutes when supplies dry up; a better way is to shift the Assemblage Point down to the centre while the central nervous system re-adapts itself.

Cannabis can produce negative neurosomatic experiences. Some of the more contemporary preparations of cannabis can, in some people, trigger panic and anxiety feelings. For example, special genetic plant strains grown under artificial light can be very stimulating. It is probable that the intense ultra violet lamps, used to encourage the plants' growth, modify the tetrahydrocannabinol molecules to a more active isomer.

Cannabis sativa or hemp is assigned to the Cannabacea plant family. There is only one other plant in this family and it is the hop plant, used to make beer. The hop plant like cannabis can have a calming or sedative effect, and the flowering heads are often placed in pillows and used by people suffering from insomnia. The tradition of making beer from hops has for some years now been dying, and the beers manufactured today do not have the same calming and satisfying effect as beers of the past. Omitting hops from beer preparations will have the effect of increasing alcohol consumption and addiction.

Recreational Drugs

Amyl and butyl nitrite (nicknamed "poppers" and "sniffers") are sometimes used by homosexuals to help induce "total orgasm" during sex. When repeatedly used to excess, this type of drug can seriously deplete biological energy. Resorting to cocaine and amphetamines in an attempt to make a recovery can result in total exhaustion. Consequently, the Assemblage Point could drop to a dangerous location. Many healthy persons have been tested and found to be H.I.V. positive and yet they have not developed A.I.D.S. It seems possible that the H.I.V. virus may not be the only or main agent that causes A.I.D.S. and that it could be a combination of H.I.V. with a low Assemblage Point location and endocrine imbalance that causes lazy lymphocyte functioning, due to depleted biological energy. Until such times as H.I.V. positive and full blown A.I.D.S. patients have their Assemblage Point locations taken into consideration, it is probable that medical researchers will continue to stumble with this dilemma. Chapter Seven discusses this in more detail.

Hallucinogenic Drugs

The location of the Assemblage Point determines how we "see" and "experience" reality. If we experience hallucinations, our Assemblage Point will be in a position which is a long way from centre. Hallucinations, dreaming and other types of three-dimensional spatial thinking activities are associated with right sided brain activity, which corresponds with an Assemblage Point location on the left side of the chest.

Hallucinogenic drugs such as L.S.D., D.M.T., D.E.T., mescaline, psilocybin, methylated amphetamines (for example, ecstasy, S.T.P., M.D.A.) and cocaine can loosen the Assemblage Point and shift it in any direction. Many factors, such as personality, guilt, fear, health and one's environment, will determine the direction and the degree of the shift of the Assemblage Point. However, in users of such drugs, the general direction of the shift is towards the left side. The larger the dose, the greater the shift and the more exaggerated the experience becomes.

When the effects of the drug have worn off, the Assemblage Point can relocate at a detrimental position and angle. Since the Assemblage Point location determines how we behave and how we feel, using these drugs can cause a sudden change in personality with the physical and psychological symptoms associated with the new location manifesting. Shifting the Assemblage Point back to the position before the drug was taken will generally correct the situation. Patients suffering long term Assemblage Point misalignment caused by drugs may require several shifts over a period of months. They may also require supportive psychological therapy to assist in the stabilisation of their Assemblage Point.

Anyone experimenting with or researching the effects of hallucinogenic drugs should be aware that their Assemblage Point location will be affected. Therefore they should keep detailed records of the Assemblage Point location, before and after drug experiences. Clinicians using these types of drugs for psychological and psychiatric research will accelerate their research programmes by taking into consideration the patient's Assemblage Point location. Without such considerations, research and therapies using hallucinogenic drugs are irresponsible and unethical.

Doctors researching L.S.D. therapy for chronic alcoholic rehabilitation should take a close look at what is happening to their patient's Assemblage Point, they will then discover the new mechanism. The success or failure of drugs like L.S.D., when used for psychological therapies, is dependent on the patient's Assemblage Point location before and after the drugs have worn off. Once the researchers get to grips with the Assemblage Point mechanism they will realise that the use of L.S.D. is not required, since they will have established that L.S.D. shifts the patient's Assemblage Point and this can be done manually without exposing the patient to further risks.

Toxins, Poisons and Pollution

Toxins, including heavy metals such as mercury and lead, petroleum products, together with gases such as carbon monoxide/dioxide, cyanide and chlorine, all depress the central nervous system. They drive the Stationary Assemblage Point down towards the critical line. Toxins created by bacteria deplete the patient's biological energy and have much the same effect on the Assemblage Point location and biological vibrational rate. In acute cases, the Assemblage Point will be left fixed close to the critical line. Should it be below on the right side it may take many months or years for the victim to recover and, if it is in the left location, the patient will be comatose. Either way, correction of the Assemblage Point will help recovery.

The following cases illustrates the irritating and destructive effects of long term exposure to chlorine gas and mercury amalgam fillings.

Case 19. Asthma and Panic Symptoms

Ms L.H., aged 22. December 1995. This young lady had developed asthma some years previously, while working as a lifeguard attendant at an indoor swimming pool. As a result she changed her job but returned to the pool for a swimming training session as she was preparing for an interview with a subaqua club. The following day, she developed a severe asthma attack. She was going to a Christmas party that evening and became breathless with panic symptoms.

Linda's respiration was short and fast with a high heart rate. Her Assemblage Point was in a high location on her right side. Due to her distressed condition, it was not appropriate to correct her alignment by shifting the Assemblage Point directly. Her symptoms were treated with electronic gem therapy, using carnelians and diamonds, with an orange filter. The stimulating orange rays were directed onto each side of her upper back in turn, in order to energise her lungs. She was treated for 20 minutes in all. After 5 minutes of treatment, she was breathing normally. Afterwards her Assemblage Point location was checked to discover that it had returned to a normal location. She told us that she thought she had developed an allergy to chlorine and household bleach.

Case 20. Myalgic encephalomyelitis (M.E.)

Mrs. R. November 1999. This female patient presented an inventory of symptoms. She was complaining of a growth on her liver, candida, breathing problems, tiredness, insomnia, cystitis, irritable bowel syndrome, unabated loss of weight, etc. According to her allergy therapist, she was allergic to almost every type of food, except for the dietary supplements which her therapist prescribed. On examination, her Assemblage Point was very low and her spleen was very agitated and hot. Her mental reasoning and personality were un-coordinated. Her dentist had fitted thirteen silver amalgam fillings, several of which were supported by metal pins inserted into the root canals of her teeth. . .

This case is typical of many female patients seen reporting with M.E., often with more than eight or nine amalgam fillings in their teeth. Women, perhaps due to their lower body weight or female hormones, are more susceptible to the toxic effects of mercury than men. Most of us have experienced damage to property due to the corrosive effects of two dissimilar metals in close contact in a wet environment. Dissimilar metals in contact create a voltage across the interface and dampness allows the electricity created to flow causing corrosion. The mouth is wet, salty and acidic, so mercury fillings secured to the root canals of a tooth with metal pins create a battery in the mouth and the electrolysis leaches mercury ions, creating various different mercury salts which are very easy for the body to absorb. Even if there are no steel pins in the fillings, when chewing food, the mercury will be absorbed by friction. In an attempt to find a cure for their symptoms, M.E. patients writing to a relevant support association were advised by return letter that there is no evidence to suggest that amalgam fillings cause M.E.. The reason that there is no evidence is simple - no studies have been done. The "pro-amalgam field" provides articles which attempt to show that amalgams do not leak toxic levels of mercury and they will provide opinion papers stating that amalgams are safe. These papers are different from research papers in that they do not present actual experimental protocols which can be tested. Invariably, they will say only an "insignificant amount of mercury is released" or something to that effect.

But there is no proof that amalgams do not contribute and "absence of proof is not proof of absence".

The various symptoms of mercury poisoning are well documented. However, if the patient has her fillings removed, but no heed is paid to the location of her Assemblage Point location before and afterwards, she still may not recover from her symptoms. Addressing the incident which caused the patient's Assemblage Point to drop will not shift it back up from low locations. Therefore, any medical data that has been gathered about the effects of the removal of amalgam fillings and any disease are inconclusive as the researchers certainly did not take into account the patient's Assemblage Point locations or correct them after removal of their mercury fillings.

The term "Quack", used to describe charlatan doctors, is in fact derived from the German word "Quacksalber", which in turn is derived from the root word "quicksilver", another name for mercury. The doctors who prescribed mercury for the treatment of syphilis, as early as the sixteenth century, were in the beginning of the twentieth century referred to as "Quacks". If the spirochaeta bacterium did not kill the patient, then the mercury did. Mercury was also used in the preparation of felt for hats, hence the terms "as mad as a hatter" and the "hatters' shakes", which are a reminder of the effects of mercury on the nervous system. Mercury metal and its various oxides and salts short circuit the nervous system and cause all kinds of confusing symptoms, as do all heavy metals including lead.

Throughout electronic, scientific and laboratory component and equipment catalogues, there are many devices which contain less mercury than is used in amalgam fillings. Products advertised as containing mercury, such as electrical tilt switches or thermometers, are advertised with stringent poison warning notices, usually in red print. The chemical industry that supplies mercury sells special mercury mop up kits, so that mercury spillages can be handled and disposed of safely. Everyone is aware of the toxic effects of the heavy metal lead, and its acetate form added to petrol has been banned in the United Kingdom. In earlier times, sugar of lead (lead acetate) was often added to bitter wines and cider to make them taste sweet and easier to sell. The results were catastrophic for the consumer and a law was introduced making this a crime punishable by hanging. The Romans had severe problems with lead poisoning as they transported wine around their empire in lead vessels. Mercury is a much more reactive and insidious poison than lead. When mercury reacts with acids, such as vinegar or citric acids, these compounds are even more lethal. Despite the fact that mercury is outlawed for dental fillings in Germany, dentists in the United Kingdom continue to fill their patients' teeth with mercury amalgam fillings. Why every industry except the United Kingdom dentistry business considers mercury to be a dangerous toxic substance is difficult to comprehend. Continuing to fit mercury fillings is stockpiling suffering and health problems for the future.

The tetanus bacillus which was responsible for many deaths years ago by causing muscle spasms and convulsions (lock-jaw), is by itself quite harmless. The toxins which it produces are 100,000 times more lethal than strychnine, which has a similar action. The toxin released by tetanus bacilli follows the path of the nearest nerve to the spinal cord. It interferes with the brain's electrical coordination of the muscles which lock rigid, pulling hard against each other. One of the first signs of this infection is lock-jaw.

Toxins are extremely dangerous and cause many varied symptoms and health problems. The body's immune defence system produces antibodies to neutralise toxins. In some cases, bacteria can find an environment inside the body where the supply cannot reach, such as in deep wounds, bone injuries, or teeth roots (infected root canal fillings). Antibiotics are useless as the blood supply cannot reach the root of the infection to kill it off. Under these circumstances the bacteria can survive for years, releasing toxins into the blood stream. Just as lock-jaw symptoms do not relate to the original injury, the patient can become insidiously sick with a variety of irreconcilable symptoms in other parts of the body and their Assemblage Point can drop. Chapter Seven gives more details regarding treatments for toxic poisoning.

High power electromagnetic fields of greater than 200 milli gauss and high voltage electrostatic fields of greater than 30,000 volts affect the weaker human field. They are a pernicious contemporary form of pollution. The human field has a very weak field of 0.1 milli gauss and nerve impulse signals at only a few millionths of a volt. The "sick building" syndrome caused by bad installation of electrical wiring and associated electrical equipment is an example of these phenomena affecting the occupants' health. Living or sleeping close to high voltage electricity pylons, transmission cables, transformer substations, overhead railway power lines or radio frequency power transmitters can be hazardous to health.

Case 21. Serious Illness following an Electric Shock

Mr J. A., aged 41. 1987. An extrovert, hard-working and creative man, John had accidentally received a severe electric shock of 10,000 volts to the back of the head. Several minutes after the shock, a dangerous psychotic episode resulted. John managed to get himself into a cold shower and recover his composure. Two days later, he went to see his doctor and reported that he felt as if he was dying. He had a deep feeling of falling away and had no physical or mental energy.

John's doctor referred him to a psychiatrist, who prescribed a powerful central nervous system depressant. John became withdrawn and forgetful, often felt suicidal and seldom left the house. Over a period of several months, John's personal and professional life started to crumble. The medications were changed periodically and his health continued to deteriorate. Eventually the psychiatrist suggested lithium medication, normally used in cases of manic depression. John refused. He tried several other therapies, including re-birthing, floatation tank and acupuncture. A year after the electric shock, circumstances eventually led John to have his Assemblage Point shifted. It had dropped to a very dangerous location only 4 cm from his navel line on the right side. His Assemblage Point was shifted up and across, a total distance of 22 cm to the centre. John had several more corrections in the months that followed, and stopped all medication. It took some 6 months to regain his former health and rebuild his personal and professional life. Thirteen years on, he is still in good health.

From John's story, it seems that the electric shock had shifted his Assemblage Point to a dangerously low location. The psychotic episode would seem to confirm this view. Most central nervous system depressants can shift the Assemblage Point to a lower position. As his Assemblage Point was only a few centimetres above the "gap", it was hardly surprising that he felt suicidal.

All of these types of fields and transmissions induce electrical eddy currents into any conductive object in close proximity, including man. Microwave ovens induce violent eddy currents in food to heat it up rapidly and the dangers of microwaves to human life are common knowledge. Colour television sets and computer monitors emit electromagnetic radiation that often extends more that four metres in all directions. Neither are the magnetic waves attenuated by brick walls. Fitting anti-glare filters does not provide any protection for the user or those nearby.

The human brain and nervous system function at very low level electrical signals levels, transmitted to and from the brain via the nervous system. High power electrical fields will modulate and distort the human field and central nervous system signals, causing biological stress. Due to natural capacitance and magnetic inductance effects, eddy currents can be induced into human tissue and bone by strong external fields. Over a period of time they can cause damage at the cellular and molecular level, the results of which might be tumours, cancer or thrombosis. The frequencies of electromagnetic fields and transmissions are also significant; they will modulate and even over-ride the natural nervous system frequencies and can cause a shift in the Assemblage Point location, along with other symptoms.

Brainwashing, Violence and Intimidation

The use of forceful indoctrination, intimidation, military training, political and religious cult brainwashing will shift the Assemblage Point in one direction or another. Military pressure groups, political fanatics, criminal organisations, covert investigation agencies and law enforcement agencies utilise authoritarian intimidation, aggressive tyrannical directives and training which drive their recruits' Assemblage Point to the extreme right, as shown in figure 3.4. This results in a disconnection from their feelings and emotions. The state of consciousness and behaviour associated with this location are always contaminated with intimidation, anger, violence and a total lack of compassion. This may be suppressed or active. The devastating effects in terms of human suffering caused by people with this location are reported in the news every day. It is an ironic fact that the salutes of extreme military factions are to the right. Assemblage Point locations on the right and associated activities are physiologically and psychologically unstable.

Subversive political organisations, multinational profiteers, pseudo-religious cults, pseudo psychological cults, secret societies, fake Gurus, fallacious pop groups and media artists, misguided psychics, bogus charities, etc., utilise subtle and obvious propaganda and brainwashing techniques. In recent years, there have been a number of horrific incidents of mass suicide, murder and homicide within a number of weird cults. They tend to employ the stimulation of guilt and fear, environmental isolation, sexual constraint, drugs, stringent dietary regulations, surrendering of personal possessions and so on, to enslave their naive followers. Their promises may include financial wealth, political freedom, perfect mental and physical health, spiritual enlightenment, self realisation, and spiritual union with God. The methods and techniques utilised shift their followers' Assemblage Point to the left side, as shown in figure 3.5. This will result in various states of fantasy, dreaming, hallucinations or melancholia.

Anyone investigating, experimenting or working with drugs, mystical

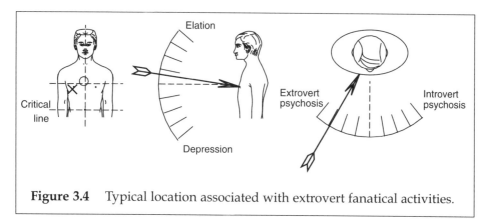

Figure 3.4   Typical location associated with extrovert fanatical activities.

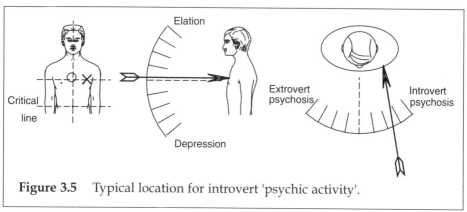

Figure 3.5   Typical location for introvert 'psychic activity'.

disciplines, spiritual cults, Tantric and Kundalini yoga or other psychic activities, should be keenly aware that the Assemblage Point location will be changed. Without ethical professional supervision and expert controls, the Assemblage Point can move to any location. Gopi Krishna in his book entitled *The Awakening Kundalini*, records his experiences following the activation of his kundalini energy by engaging in mystical disciplines which increased his biological energy:

Gopi Krishna's experience was disturbing. He reported that it was painful, obsessive and psychotic and at times he was fluctuating between sanity and insanity. However, soon after his illness began, his physical and mental condition stabilised, whereupon he said that his consciousness expanded and became more and more beautiful and alluring. Based on his own experience he mistakenly stated that the kundalini energy was the basis of genius, insanity and neurosis, and other extra ordinary states of consciousness.

There are very few mystics, teachers or gurus who know anything about the dominions of the Assemblage Point. There are many psychics and mystics in these times (and in the past) who claim to be able to see numerous aspects of the human energy field or aura. The Assemblage Point is the highest energy centre of the human body. It is difficult to decipher the reasons why the Assemblage Point has eluded their visionary expertise. The actual mechanics involved, when changing states of consciousness, are a shift in the Assemblage Point location. If one stimulates the Kundalini energy by any method, it is essential to take into consideration the Assemblage Point location. The extra pressure caused by increasing the levels of biological energy will cause the Assemblage Point to move around. When this happens one can expect aberrations similar to Gopi Krishna's experience.

If one wishes to deliberately stimulate and increase levels of biological energy, it is prudent, if not essential, to maintain the Assemblage Point in the centre. Keeping this fact in mind will greatly reduce the dangers and risks which are associated with these activities. Correcting and maintaining the Assemblage Point location to the central position will restore rational feelings, emotions and behaviour. Over time, central locations increase mental and physical performance. Teachers and students of professional and competitive sport, martial arts, mystical disciplines, Tantric yoga and Kundalini yoga and so on, must realise that their Assemblage Point location will affect overall performance and skill development.

Almost all of these types of activity involve deliberate manipulation and accumulation of biological energy. The accumulation of biological energy will cause the energy field to expand. This can result in the Assemblage Point moving away from the surface of the body. This produces another range of experiences which are more to do with the acquisition and control of psychic powers. This subject will be discussed in future publications. As far as the average person is concerned, there is no evidence to suggest that there are any medical benefits of Assemblage Point locations other than at the centre, or, at least, around the typical male and female locations mentioned in the next chapter.

Patients' Rules for Practitioners

Following a series of articles on the Assemblage Point, published in *Positive Health* (1996), alarming reports came in from patients seeking Assemblage Point correction. Several bogus alternative and complementary practitioners and small minded business operators were capitalising on the publicity by selling pills, bottled medicines or various gadgets to wear or keep on one's person, all supposedly being able to correct the Assemblage Point. Other reports involved bogus psychics and healers claiming to shift Assemblage Points over the telephone or by distance healing. All such methods were nonsense and unethical. Even worse, one well known alternative medical practitioner, with extensive international commercial investments in the consumption and sales of numerous herbal preparations, was deliberately misrepresenting the Assemblage Point facts to patients and other practitioners in favour of selling his own products and therapies. Today's all too common practice of compromising a patient's health for financial profit by prescribing extended therapies and other medications which do not work is abhorrent.

Clinical correction of a patient's Assemblage Point location requires two dedicated and medically ethical therapists. It also requires intense personal energy and patient co-operation. Seeing and treating a dozen patients is a hard day's work, by anyone's standards. Patients requiring Assemblage Point correction therapies should look out for the following minimum standards when choosing a therapist to do the work.

Choose a registered clinic, doctor or therapist with a reputation for the work or go by recommendation from a good source. The clinical working space should be clean, large, light and well ventilated. The room should also be fitted with an examination couch, working desk and at least three chairs and should be free of any electromagnetic or electrostatic polluting electrical equipment. One principal therapist and assistant therapist or nurse should be present during the locating and shifting procedures. Both should be trained and experienced in locating and shifting Assemblage Points. Two therapists are required to double-check each other's work and the location before and after each shift. The therapists should be radiantly enthusiastic, physically and mentally healthy. All good practitioners record details of their patients, for later reference. Make sure that your details are recorded on official forms; if not, there could be good reason for suspicion.

chapter 4

LOCATING AND EXPERIENCING THE ASSEMBLAGE POINT

Every so often, a beneficial discovery or invention comes along which changes the course of fortunes and history. Discovering and proving that every human has an energy body together with an Assemblage Point is a major breakthrough. The ability to change how we feel and how we behave by adjusting or correcting our energy body alignment is nothing short of miraculous. The numerous limitations and hardships imposed by detrimental Assemblage Point locations either on oneself or on others becomes untenable.

The foregoing chapters have indicated some of the thousands of ways that the human Assemblage Point can be shifted to disturbing locations. As far as most of us are concerned, detrimental shifts in our Assemblage Point are involuntary or accidental. When they occur, we are ignorant of the mechanisms of the shift, and are dominated by the symptoms and consequences which occur as a result. Until now, there has not been any reliable and easy method of returning to normal health, or re-establishing our old Assemblage Point location.

Knowledge of and familiarity with the Assemblage Point, are the catalysts to personal power and freedom. The action of consciously shifting the Assemblage Point is a catalyst for changing our state of consciousness. Not only can the techniques be used for health reasons, regular periodic shifts in the Assemblage Point location will precipitate accelerated personal development and self control in all aspects of living. Thus the psychological, medical, political and economic benefits are enormous.

Once we are familiar with our own Assemblage Point location and that of others, the idea that there is more to a human being than flesh and bone becomes an absolute certainty.

The law of energy conservation states that energy can neither be created nor destroyed. It can only be changed in form. When we are alive, we have "life energy" in our body. When we are dead that energy is gone. Physics says it does not cease to be; it can only change form. Therefore, there is a part of us, the energy part, which exists beyond the body.

Locating and experiencing our Assemblage Point provides us with personal proof that we all have an energy body as well as a physical body. Working with the energy body is not a trivial affair. The Assemblage Point, in particular, is a very personal matter, directly connected to the "life force" or spirit of the individual.

Case 22

Mrs D.B., University Lecturer, retired. November 1995. This lady reported, "I asked Jon about spiritual matters, especially reincarnation. Handing me two powerful therapeutic magnets, he said, "The eye cannot see magnetic waves, but we can experience their effects". Then he instructed me to place one magnet in each hand and to bring my hands slowly together. Suddenly the magnet in my left hand jumped out and across several inches to crash against the second magnet in my right hand. The magnetic power was too strong for me to physically control. He then said, "Enveloping every living person is a strong energy field that is visible only under special circumstances". He emphasised that, just as I had experienced the power of the magnets, I could, any time I liked, experience the power of the human energy field.

As a practising Christian, I felt great doubt, but also curiosity, and took up his challenge. Following instructions, I brought my hands towards his chest and upper back. As my right hand came within 12 inches of his chest, a "power" took over and I could not control my arms. I felt strong tingling sensations pass up my right arm and across my chest, connecting to my left hand at his back. My hands automatically came into and touched the centre of his chest and back. I admit I was frightened. Something beyond me, a field of energy, took control of my hands and arms.

Over the next 2 weeks, I became very aware of my own Assemblage Point location. I was aware of a curved energy line entering my upper right chest through to my shoulder blade. This energy line seemed connected to a kindred spirit "out there". The next time I saw Jon, I asked him if he would confirm my location. He told me the precise location and angle of entry, then came over to me and touched the exact spot. Becoming aware of my own assemblage point has confirmed my belief that we all have a "spirit energy" outside or above the physical body that dies. My discovery complements my Christian faith."

Characteristics of the Assemblage Point

The Assemblage Point is not part of the physical body. It is an integral component of the energy body which surrounds the physical body. It manifests, in so far as it is possible to define, as a large indentation of energy lines, which pierce the physical body. Figure 4.1 is exaggerated for clarity. Its entry position is "fixed" or "stationary" on most people.

The average diameter of the bundle of energy lines is 1 cm. These appear to cause a sausage-shaped indentation in the energy field, which passes through the chest into the body and out through the back. There is a definite energy "potential" both along the length of the lines and across

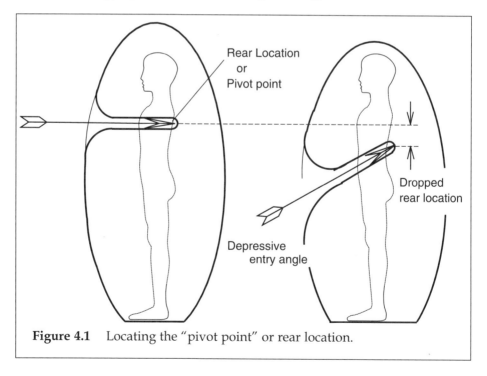

Figure 4.1   Locating the "pivot point" or rear location.

their diameter. This energy potential can be easily discerned by examination using the hands or by a trained eye. Where the bundle of lines enters the physical body, they induce a tender or very sensitive area of skin of the same diameter. This tenderness can be quite uncomfortable and can often penetrate through to the shoulder blade if the spot is touched with the finger and light pressure is applied.

Where to Look for the Assemblage Point

The location of a woman's Assemblage Point is generally, but not always, several centimetres higher than that of a man (Figure 4.2.). Broadly speaking, a woman's vibrational rate, her behaviour, the way she feels and her view of the world are quite different to a man's. Therefore, female and male locations tend to be different. Finding the precise location and entry angle of the average, healthy, balanced person is a very quick and simple affair.

Patients with a bright and energetic disposition (a high vibrational rate)

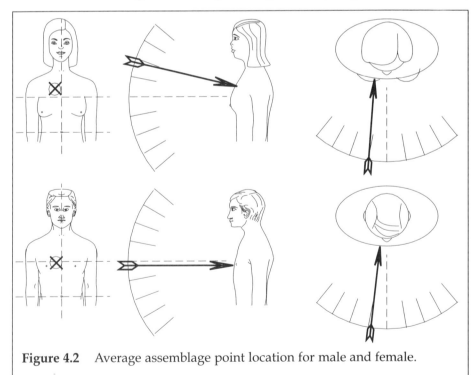

Figure 4.2   Average assemblage point location for male and female.

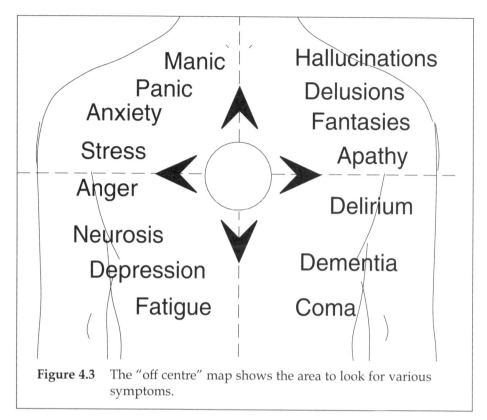

Figure 4.3   The "off centre" map shows the area to look for various symptoms.

will have a high location and elevated entry angle. Depressed and lethargic patients, such as those suffering from M.E. or post-natal depression, will have a low location and descending entry angle. Finding the location and entry angle for patients with mental or physical health problems can be difficult in the beginning, but gets easier as one gains experience. Often their symptoms, posture, and tone of voice will suggest where to look. The "off centre" map (figure 4.3) gives a general overview of locations for specific physical and psychological symptoms. There are, however, rare exceptions to these.

Investigators of the intuitive or feeling types (as defined by C.G. Jung) generally will not experience any difficulties in locating Assemblage Points. Rational and practical personality types will find difficulties with the feeling and seeing methods described below. This is explained in more detail in Chapter Five. Confidence will develop with experience. Therefore, in the beginning, it is best to work in a small team, assisting each other and comparing results and notes. Maintain good records for each patient. Note their medication, symptoms, age, sex, and profession.

Record your results using photocopies of the special forms provided at the back of this book. When shifting Assemblage Points, make a drawing of the location and entry angle before and after shifting it or using other medication or therapies. Those of you who do not have any health problems, but are using the techniques for self improvement or any other reasons, are recommended to keep written details together with any relevant notes for future reference.

The following methods and procedures for locating the Assemblage Point are very easy to learn. Many people by simply following these instructions and without any intervention or training have been successful with their first attempt at Assemblage Point locating. With time and experience it soon becomes possible to see other people's Assemblage Points. These methods will be quickly confirmed and improved on by many other investigators. Photographic and electronic evidence of the Assemblage Point is likely to follow this publication as electronic engineers take up the research.

Finding the Location of the Assemblage Point

1. The subject or patient should stand upright, looking straight ahead at the horizon. The investigator should stand facing the patient's right hand body side, see figure 4.4.

2. Form your left hand into a cup shape (figure 4.5). Use it to "feel" for the sausage shaped end of the subject or patient's Assemblage Point in the area of the shoulder blades, as shown in figure 4.1.

3. Form the fingers and thumb of your right hand into a tight, concentrated point as in figure 4.5. Use the tips of the bunched fingers to "feel" for the bundle of energy lines entering or exiting the subject.

4. Hold both of your arms wide apart. Hold your left hand behind the subject and your right hand out in front. Standing relaxed, be keenly aware of your physical feelings and your weight on the floor. It helps to close your eyes or look away. Slowly bring your hands towards the subject, feeling for the maximum energy. Allow the patient's energy to control your arm muscles. It helps to keep your left hand very close but not touching the subject's back. Seek for the Assemblage Point energy by slowly moving both hands around in a circular motion as you bring them closer to the subject.

5. The difference in energy potential along the bundle of lines of the Assemblage Point makes it easy to distinguish. When your cupped hand and pointed fingers are lined up with the subject's or patient's bundle of energy lines, you will experience an energy surge. This will pass through your arms and chest. Sensitive patients will also feel this surge. You should feel like a very mild electrical current is flowing in your fingers and along your arms. You may hear internally, a faint hissing sound as you come onto the subject's Assemblage Point.

6. Bring your hands together, feeling for the maximum power and connection with the patient. Allow your hands to touch the patient's back and chest at the points of maximum energy connection.

7. Move your right hand fingers back and forth across the patient or subjects Assemblage Point. As you move your right hand fingers back and forth across your subject's Assemblage Point,

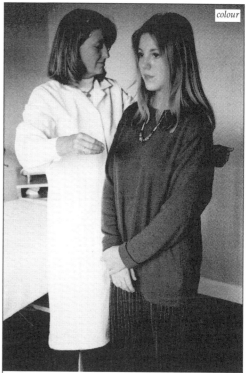

Figure 4.4   The correct way to stand when locating the assemblage point.

you will clearly be able to distinguish the energy pressure change as you go across it each time. Sensitive patients will feel a "pulling" sensation deep inside the chest as you move back and forth across it. When you are sure that you have located it, use small, adhesive labels to mark the positions at the back and front of your subject.

Clothes manufactured from synthetic materials can hold sufficient static electricity that they will cause interference and prevent or cause errors in Assemblage Point detection. Synthetic jumpers and shirts should be removed. Light cotton and wool clothes do not cause much interference and need not be removed. However heavy coats and sweaters should be removed. Sometimes, perhaps when training and learning amongst friends, it is helpful to expose the chest area for examination and identification of the area of skin where the Assemblage Point enters (see the subtitle below: Locating the Assemblage Point using Biofeedback).

Finding the Assemblage Point by Muscle Testing

This procedure is not suitable for frail or exhausted patients. Considerable energy is required by the patient to hold their arm out horizontally for any period of time, therefore this procedure is not used for clinical work.

Figure 4.5   How to 'form your hands' for locating the assemblage point.

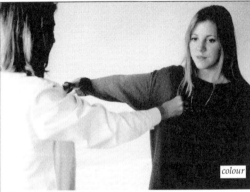

Figure 4.6   'Muscle testing' for the Assemblage Point location.

1.Stand facing the subject. With your left arm, apply slight pressure to the subject's outstretched right arm, as shown in Figure 4.6. The patient or subject should resist your downward pressure on their arm.

2.Grouping the fingers to a point, as before, move your right hand across the subject's chest. Keep the hand at a distance of two to five centimetres away from the chest. The subject's arm will suddenly go weak and drop when you move across the location. The interference of the subject's energy field causes the muscles to give way momentarily.

3. Check the entry angle by testing the patient's arm muscle strength further away from the chest at around twenty centimetres distance. Drawing your fingers in and out along the Assemblage Point lines will reflect in the

patient's arm muscle tone. This will enable you to ascertain the entry angle.

4. Touching the subject's chest at the entry location using your finger will cause the subject's arm muscles to weaken and their arm will drop suddenly.

Locating the Assemblage Point using Biofeedback

Touching or pushing the Assemblage Point with a finger will stimulate a stress/arousal response in the patient's body. This arousal response will cause the patient's skin resistance to change. This change can be detected by many of the biofeedback devices available today. Researchers and clinicians working with the more expensive, electronic biofeedback systems, infrared scanners or other electronic measuring equipment will be able to provide additional scientific proof of the Assemblage Point's existence and location.

The skin at the point of entry on the chest has different electrical properties to that of the surrounding skin. These differences are measurable with sensitive electronic instrumentation, as described in the Appendices to this book. However, this is a very sensitive area of the body and prolonged experimentation with electrical test meters or other equipment is very irritating. Most people probably will not easily tolerate too much investigation of this vital energy point.

Seeing the Assemblage Point Location

The ability to see Assemblage Points permits a completely new perspective on human affairs. A whole new world of understanding is made available. The interactive properties of the various Assemblage Point locations and the way they affect human relationships, social and public behaviour, business interaction, situations of conflict and so on becomes exposed. Being able to see the Assemblage Point of other people exposes to us their state of consciousness. For example, if a person's Assemblage Point is habitually located towards the far right side of their chest (extrovert psychosis), one can expect trouble sooner or later. The Assemblage Point and its effects on our relationships and interaction with other people is a very interesting and profound subject. Once a person has acquired and integrated the Assemblage Point knowledge and can see other Assemblage Points, there automatically follows a leap in ability to understand and manage situations without getting involved.

Looking for or seeing the Assemblage Point is the most difficult method to describe and comprehend yet, ironically, it is the simplest and least obtrusive way to locate Assemblage Points. The method, though totally subjective, is most useful in assessment and diagnosis. If you can "see" your patient's Assemblage Point alignment, it becomes possible, with experience, to know the patient's symptoms in advance of them telling you. A female medical doctor who had had her right arm amputated due to skin cancer, having only one arm and unable to locate Assemblage Points using the methods outlined above, right from the beginning, when she was first introduced to the Assemblage Point techniques, was an insuperable expert at seeing them.

1) Always look for the Assemblage Point before you use any of the above methods to locate it. Confirming the location by using the other methods will develop your confidence and accuracy in "seeing" it.

2) It is essential to realise that what we see of the outside world is not the real thing. Everything that we experience, including what we see, is a model or hologram, a mental construct inside our mind. While intensely observing your patient or subject, suspend all thinking and judgements. Try to perceive the space surrounding your patient as being charged with energy. It helps if you can imagine that you can see the air or atmosphere surrounding your subject.

3) Try to see the energy as effervescent particles. Look for a concentration of these particles in front of and on the surface of your subject or patient. Where the particles are most concentrated you will find the Assemblage Point location. These particles may be bright or dull. Look for lines of flux, flowing to a small concentrated bright spot or even a shadow on the patient. Take careful note of the location and try to discern the angle of entry as this information will enable you to evaluate their condition.

Confirming the Location

At the location of the Assemblage Point, the skin is less resilient and more painful to the touch. The skin may occasionally be blemished or marked in some way, sometimes by a reddish spot. Touching or pushing the spot with a finger will cause the skin to redden more than skin elsewhere on the chest. The spot is tender, sore or uncomfortable. Pushing it causes the patient a feeling of slight unease. The feeling passes deep into the chest, often right through to the shoulder blade. Any sensitive person touching the precise location of a patient's Assemblage Point will feel an exchange of energy. It will feel like a faint or weak electric shock and often has a buzzing or vibrating quality to it.

Patients' Considerations

Patients with low locations will most often react physically when their Assemblage Point is found. For example, they may start to tremble or shake as you move your right hand across their Assemblage Point. Sometimes they complain of a long-standing pain in their back where your left hand is, their Assemblage Point's "pivot point". Therefore, do not practice on patients - learn the methods with your friends and colleagues first. When you are confident that you can locate the Assemblage Point efficiently, then progress to work with pathological patients.

Shadows And Splits

From time to time, in the clinical setting, patients can present a shadow or split Assemblage Point. These are most often associated with patients suffering from schizophrenia or manic depression. In numerous cases of schizophrenia, two locations of the Assemblage Point have been observed on each patient: one shadow location high up, near the patient's right collar bone and a second brighter location lower down on the same side. Diagnosed manic depressive patients often have two locations: one strong and active, and the second a shadow location. The locations are generally lower and not so far to the right side as in diagnosed schizophrenic patients. In such cases, patients display two distinct sets of symptoms (e.g. mania and depression in manic depressive disorder, also known in psychiatry as bipolar affective disorder). These patients, by one means or another, unconsciously shift their Assemblage Point locations. This, in turn, changes their behaviour and the way they feel. In this way, the patient oscillates between two locations. Split locations can be reunited and shifted across to a more central and stable location for the patient. From a central position, the patient's mental and physical health will stabilise.

Infants and Children

The Assemblage Point in babies and young children has no fixed location. It is unstable and can move freely. As a child's personality and internal dialogue develop, the Assemblage Point begins to be fixed. Given a stable environment, most children's location will become fixed when they are around 6 years of age, or slightly later. Ideally, adolescents and juveniles should be allowed to develop and fix their own location, without interference other than the normal family and educational procedures. As with adults, children with serious misalignment of their Assemblage Point do not find it easy to integrate with their peers. Youngsters who have experienced accidents, intimidation, drug abuse, illness, or psychological problems are likely to have misalignment and stability problems. In such cases, any educational or therapeutic methods which will stabilise and centralise their Assemblage Point will help their development. Children over ten years of age with health problems or symptoms caused by misalignment can gain substantial benefits from the shifting and realignment procedures coupled with other supportive therapy. In any event, with the onset of puberty, a child's Assemblage Point will move to a new location which reflects the physical and psychological changes that invariably accompany puberty.

The Frequency of Health

The following series of drawings (figures 4.7 to 4.13) show approximate or typical locations for some common conditions. Diagnosis varies from one doctor to another, therefore as long as the diagnosis is accurate then the drawings will greatly assist trainees to locate pathological Assemblage Point locations.

Agitation, anxiety and panic symptoms have a high physical and mental vibrational or frequency rate, the person is "wound up". These drawings illustrate the relationship of high Assemblage Point locations and elevated entry angles with agitated symptoms which are

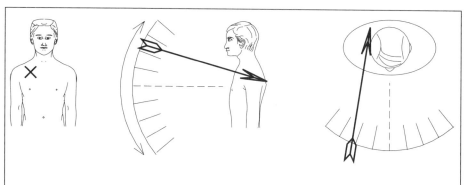

Figure 4.7   Manic symptoms, typical location, entry angle and rear
location.

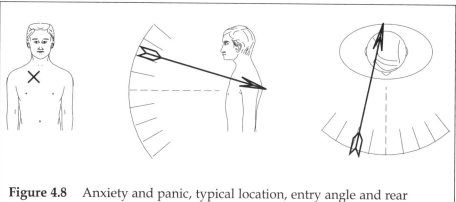

Figure 4.8   Anxiety and panic, typical location, entry angle and rear
location.

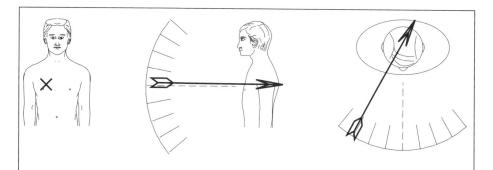

Figure 4.9   Executive stress, typical location, entry angle and rear
location.

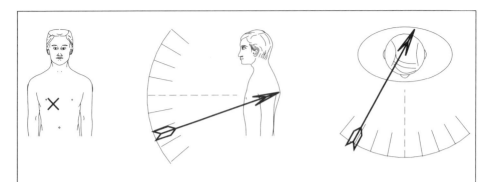

Figure 4.10 Agitated depression, typical location, entry angle and rear location.

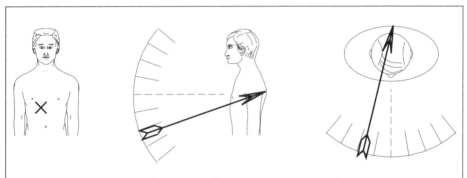

Figure 4.11 Clinical and post-natal depression, typical location, entry angle and rear location.

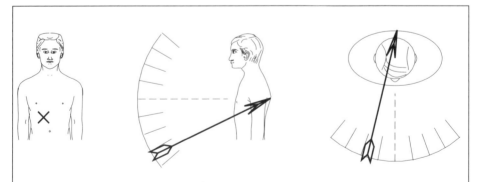

Figure 4.12 M.E., or myalgic encephomyelitis, typical location, entry angle and rear location.

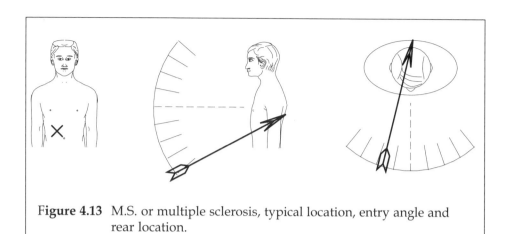

Figure 4.13 M.S. or multiple sclerosis, typical location, entry angle and rear location.

accompanied with excessive high biological energy and high brain frequencies.

They also illustrate how these conditions contrast with depressive diseases with their correspondingly low locations and low entry angles, which are accompanied with chronic low biological energy and chronic low brain frequencies.

Another very important point to take note of is that, if the Assemblage Point's rear location or pivot point drops down from the shoulder blade area, muscular coordination becomes affected. When it drops down to a definite critical area, around four centimetres below the shoulder blades, the patient's nervous system, which controls their muscles, becomes unstable and starts to self-oscillate. The tone of the muscles can become stiff and sluggish, movement becomes clumsy and difficult. The brain compensates by sending stronger electrical signals to the muscles, which causes them to contract too much or overshoot. The brain immediately sends another signal to correct for the overshoot and this creates a self oscillating system. Groups of muscles rhythmically tremble and twitch involuntarily, which produces the characteristics of Parkinsonism. As the Assemblage Point rear location progresses further down towards the lower back, the patient can loose control of their movements altogether, and they become paralysed. When the rear location drops below a line drawn across the kidneys (first, lumbar vertebra), death occurs. As long as the pivot point is above this line, life can be sustained.

The Assemblage Point is an excellent diagnostic tool as its location indicates the person's overall frequency. Shifting the Assemblage Point to a more stable location is a superb means of controlling and adjusting the frequency of the human body.In this set of drawings the arrow passes through the figure of the man, to his back. This is an important point to remember.

1) In the drawings, the point at which the tip of the arrow marks or touches the man's back is where the rear pivot point will be found. It is around this area for each of the illustrated cases that you will have to feel with the palm of your left hand.

2) Where it passes through the front of the man's chest area in the drawings is where you will have to feel using the tips of the fingers of your right hand.

After some practice, you will feel sufficiently competent to locate anyone's Assemblage Point. Being able to locate Assemblage Points provides the foundation required to shift and manipulate them. The ability to locate, manipulate and shift the Human Assemblage Point is a profoundly beneficial skill.

chapter 5

Correcting
The Assemblage Point For Health

The foregoing case studies have demonstrated that debilitating disease causes the Assemblage Point to descend in degrees towards the navel. The more serious and complicated the symptoms, the closer the Assemblage Point will be located to the navel line.

Clinically depressed patients, such as M.E. sufferers, will have a dropped or low Assemblage Point location (figure 5.1). Patients with anxiety or panic symptoms will have a high location. The case studies prove that shifting the patient's Assemblage Point to the central position will dramatically assist their recovery. Observing patients recover as their Assemblage Point stabilises in a new location provides the final proof. It proves that:

1. Surrounding every human being is an energy field, the epicentre of which is the Assemblage Point;

2. Misalignment of the energy body and dislocation of the Assemblage Point adversely affect the way we think, feel and behave;

3. A centralised Assemblage Point location has a beneficial influence on our biological energy levels and physical health;

4. The central location is also beneficial for mental health - it directly influences our interactions with others and the world at large.

Those of us who are fortunate enough to possess a stable, centrally aligned Assemblage Point prosper in health, performance and success. The average person's location is to the right of centre. Many retired people maintain a good high location and by doing so remain active and happy, well into old age.

People with unstable or misaligned Assemblage Points do not get the best from life. Misalignment detrimentally affects physical and mental performance. Dropped Assemblage Points, in particular, cause unnecessary suffering and are a tragic waste of human potential and resources. Long-term gross misalignment can cause serious physiological and psychological symptoms. It is often reflected in a hunched or

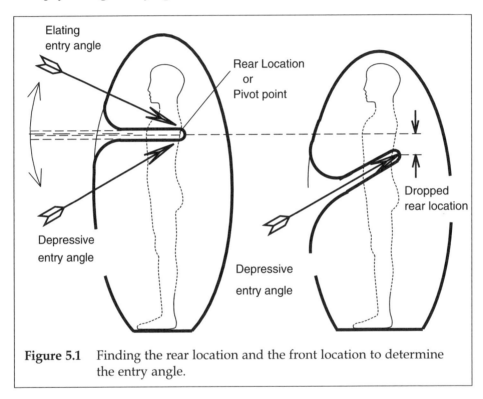

Figure 5.1   Finding the rear location and the front location to determine the entry angle.

slumped body posture.

Shifting the Assemblage Point will change the patient's complexion, posture and medication requirements. For some patients, for example, those who are suicidal, shifting the Assemblage Point can be life saving. Before diagnosing and prescribing any treatment, one of the clinician's first considerations should be the assessment and correction of their patient's Assemblage Point location. In many cases, medication will not be required after correction.

Locating and shifting the Assemblage Point takes about five minutes.

The procedures are painless. The experience can be exhilarating and stabilising. For some patients, depending on the location of their Assemblage Point and the symptoms or disease which they are experiencing, the experience can be a profound relief. The procedures are compatible with most therapies. The case studies confirm the enormous. potential for medical and financial benefits for the patient, the medical insurance companies, the National Health Services and the tax payer.

Accelerating Personal Development

Regular central shifting of the Assemblage Point will significantly improve mental and physical efficiency. The following reports are from professional people having an Assemblage Point location within or just outside the area for normal healthy individuals.

Case 23

Mr. N.D., Company Director. October 1998. Mr N.D. reported that, "Normally I have trouble with my vision - I have to wear glasses or contact lenses. When I had my assemblage point corrected, I was instantly stunned when my vision cleared and I could see without glasses. Although I had thought that I was a healthy, fit and balanced person, I was impressed with the new feeling of being centred. I still do not fully understand what this energy centre is. Being sceptical, I was delighted to discover and become aware of my assemblage point. I can see that it has a definite place in my future".

Case 24

Mrs. K.B. Therapist. May 1998. This lady reported, "I am a slightly nervous person, but I can tolerate the underlying feelings quite well. Over the years, I have learnt to cope by being careful with what I eat and being sure to get enough sleep and rest. What I was most taken with after the shift was a feeling of solidness and physical strength. It is a feeling that I have never experienced before. My mind was naturally quiet and I felt more aware of the world and less preoccupied with my feelings. I know that this is a subject that I will be investigating. I can think of a number of my clients that would benefit from this therapy".

Case 25

Ms V.C., aged 34, Therapist. March 1987. "Before the shift I felt off centre, a bit low in my mood, self conscious, and anxious. I also felt separated from many people in the group. After the shift, I saw things much differently; I felt centred and easy with myself. My spirit lifted, and my eyes got much brighter. I seemed to have more energy, and I could feel more empathy with the whole group. I no longer felt anxious and could perceive myself in relation to others differently."

Central locations improve reflex times, muscular co-ordination, posture, confidence and, in particular, assertiveness. The central location will increase performance in employment or a profession, sports or other team activities, martial arts, dancing, singing, yoga, and meditation. Esoteric disciplines, such as T'ai chi, Kundalini, Raja, Chakra and Tantric yogas, all use special techniques to increase psychic powers and control vital life force energies. The energy body and Assemblage Point extend beyond the physical body as an energy field. This field can influence other people and events. Paying close attention to the Assemblage Point location will speed up and enhance results from these disciplines.

The Shaman's Blow

It is possible for a trained person to shift the Assemblage Point without any aids or tools. The following letter received from a victim of a car accident illustrates the techniques used by ancient American Indian Shamen.

I have been reading Castaneda's book The Fire From Within, *he talks about shifting the Assemblage Point with a blow to the apprentices' backs. In this book Carlos says that the old Shamen shifted their apprentices' assemblage points which catapulted them into an enhanced, discerning, most malleable state of consciousness with a blow to the right shoulder blade. He says the force of the push knocks all of the air out of the lungs.*

Elsewhere in this book he says that a dropped assemblage point due to an accident or drug overdose is very dangerous to health. Two years ago, I was involved in a car accident. I received a heavy blow and injuries to my back and since then, I have not been well. I would like to know if it is possible that my

Assemblage Point could have been shifted to a low location?

This somewhat frightening account, which is typical of Castaneda's style of writing, talks about shifting the Assemblage Point with a blow to the right shoulder blade. Most people's Assemblage Point enters the right side of the chest and penetrates through to the right shoulder blade. This is the "pivot point" or "rear location" (figure 5.1). The rear location must be found in order to shift the Assemblage Point (see Chapter Four).

A trained and strongly centred person can shift and centralise anyone's Assemblage Point by slapping or thumping the rear location or pivot point, using the palm of the right hand. The clenched left hand is placed on the centre of the subject's chest. The technique requires great mental concentration and personal energy, as well as the full co-operation of the person receiving the shift.

Some native American medicine men can shift Assemblage Points with a single blow, catching their subjects by surprise. The shaman fixes the direction and location of the shift using his "unbending intent". This type of shifting technique, although effective and spectacular, is not suitable for clinical work. It is too abrupt and requires too much personal energy and self-discipline to be effective. In a clinical setting patients frequently have a low location and poor health. In such cases a softer approach is called for, using the special techniques and tools recommended.

Shifting Tools

The following procedures require the use of a large quartz crystal. The procedures should not be confused with the recent "New Age" therapy called Crystal Healing. Some Crystal Healers are not medically trained or equipped with the clinical hardware and support personnel to treat pathological Assemblage Point locations or provide the support therapies which seriously ill patients may require.

To undo or tighten a nut or bolt, we use a spanner. Precision realigning and shifting of Assemblage Points is best done with a specially machined quartz crystal. It is possible to use objects other than a quartz crystal to shift Assemblage Points. However, the natural polarising properties of quartz are ideally suited for Assemblage Point manipulation. Figure 5.3 illustrates the principles of arresting or capturing the Assemblage Point energy. For consistent results observe the following minimum standards for the crystal. The crystal should weigh 200 g or more, have a length of at least 18 cm and a diameter of 3 cm or more. The crystal must have a ground and polished convex or domed end. It should be as clear as

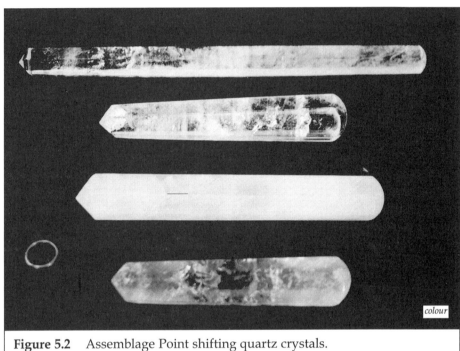

Figure 5.2   Assemblage Point shifting quartz crystals.

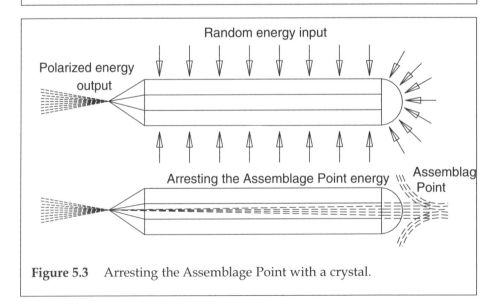

Figure 5.3   Arresting the Assemblage Point with a crystal.

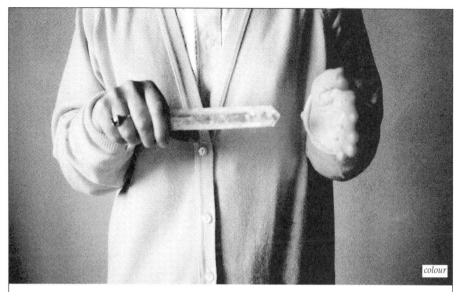

Figure 5.4   Checking the crystal for energy activity.

possible. It must have a well-defined point. The point should have at least three perfect triangles amongst its six facets (Figure 5.2 and 5.3)

The crystal must be "alive" or "active". To check this, hold the crystal with your right hand and direct the point at the palm of your left hand. You should feel a breeze of cool, tingling energy penetrating the skin of your left hand (figure 5.4.).

Charging a crystal with your biological energy will increase its activity. To do this, hold the crystal tight in your right hand, as you would a screwdriver, and breathe in and out slowly and very deeply three times. Hold the third breath, contract your anal sphincter muscles, swallow simultaneously, and direct your energy up your body and down your right arm into the crystal, at the same time firmly squeezing the crystal. This will increase the energy emitted from the point. Closing the anal muscles and swallowing at the same time prevents your biological energy from exiting via these portals, so that it can be directed up the body down the arm and into the crystal. Once again, check the crystal for activity; it should by now be substantially more active.

If a quartz crystal is unobtainable, a confident practitioner will be able to shift the Assemblage Point with a large smooth round stone of similar diameter to the above specifications, such as can be found on seashores. White quartz is very common on shorelines. Other objects which can be used to aid shifting are ornamental crystal or semiprecious stone eggs, ferrite rods and perhaps large bar or circular magnets.

The Sliding Shift

Shifting the Assemblage Point by sliding it from one location to another is the easiest and most straightforward method. It is the preferred method for training purposes and best practiced with friends and colleagues or in a group workshop situation. This method has several disadvantages in a clinical setting. The subject must be bare chested and it is time consuming to get the patient to remove the clothing from the chest area . Also, it can be difficult to use on female patients whose Assemblage Point location has dropped below their breast, as in M.E.. Sliding or manipulating a dropped Assemblage Point up across a female breast is bit tricky, but it can be done.

To use this method of realignment, the subject or patient must co-operate. Practitioners should adhere to the following instructions and rules, so as not to develop any bad habits.

1. Locate the subject's Assemblage Point as instructed in Chapter Two. Mark the locations on his chest and back with a marking pen or small adhesive labels.

2. Instruct the subject to stand upright, head up and chin tucked in back slightly, looking straight ahead.

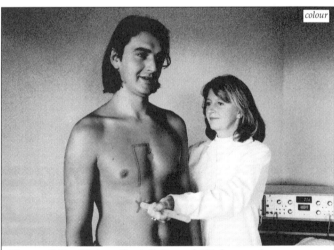

| **Figure 5.5** | Using the 'sliding shift' from a low location. |

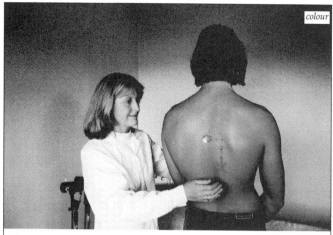

Figure 5.6   Using the right hand to raise the rear
'pivot point' location.

3. Stand facing the left hand side of the subject's body. Holding the quartz crystal in your left hand, place the polished, domed end on the precise location of the subject's Assemblage Point (figure 5.5.).

4. Use the palm of your right hand to cover and slide the rear location around the shoulder blade area (figure 5.6.).

5. Instruct your subject to take three deep breaths, slowly in through the nose and out of the mouth. Make sure that they are good and deep, if not get them to take three more or how ever many is necessary to achieve full expansion of their lungs and chest cavity. Between each inhalation and exhalation the patient should pause for one second. Inhale to the count of seven, pause one count, exhale to the count of seven, pause for one count, inhale to the count of seven, and so on for three full deep breath cycles.

6. On the third breath, when the chest is expanded and the lungs are full with air, instruct your subject to hold the breath in. Next instruct him to contract his sphincter and other muscles in the anus and genital area, and keep them contracted. Then instruct him to swallow and close the throat at the same time (head upright and chin back).

7. This effectively closes the upper and lower exit and entry gateways to the body. With the retained breath and closed gateways, pressure builds up and pushes or loosens the subject's energy field from his physical body. This situation will allow you to slide the Assemblage Point to the central location using a quartz crystal. Most subjects can hold their breath

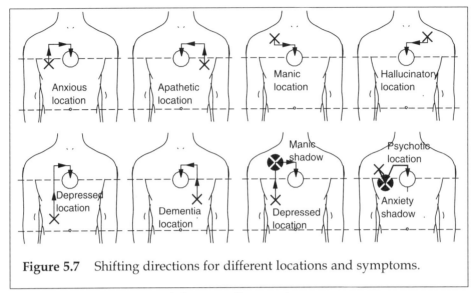

Figure 5.7 Shifting directions for different locations and symptoms.

for five or ten seconds and this is sufficient time.

8. Using the quartz crystal, slide your subject's Assemblage Point to the centre of the chest. Use the palm of your right hand to drag the rear location into the centre between the shoulder blades. Twist the crystal half a turn and remove it from his chest. Simultaneously, tap him lightly on his head with the palm of your right hand and tell him to breathe normally.

The shift should be in the directions shown in figure 5.7. Never shift in a diagonal direction. It helps to lubricate the domed end of the crystal with a fine vegetable or massage oil. It can then slide easily over the skin.

Sometimes, when shifting the Assemblage Point, some subjects will not be able to maintain holding the throat or the sphincter muscles closed. Or they will fail to retain the held breath or let out their breath. When this occurs the Assemblage Point may be lost at any point during the sliding shifting procedure. This can and does often happen, especially with frail or nervous people. In such cases, the Assemblage Point must be relocated using the instructions in chapter four and the shifting procedure repeated.

How to Instruct Your Subject Or Patient

Guide your subject or patient in the following way, by reading out to them the following instructions. The procedure is much easier if the subject or patient is reassured. Explain and to them beforehand what you are going to ask them to do, saying something on the lines of:

"I need your cooperation and assistance in order to move your Assemblage Point. I am going to instruct you to take three deep breaths, through your nose, pausing between each breath. When you have taken the third breath, I will instruct you to hold your breath. At the same time I will ask you to squeeze or contract the muscles in your anus and genitals, as if you are needing to go the toilet and are not able to. I will then ask you swallow and keep your throat closed and continue to hold your breath, I will then shift your assemblage point".

Once the patient or subject has understood this, proceed to shift their Assemblage Point and instruct them, by reading to them the following:

"Please stand upright, arms relaxed by your sides, with your back and shoulders straight and chest pushed out. Relax, with your feet placed slightly apart. Now become even more relaxed and feel and be aware of the weight of your body standing on the floor. Breathe normally and look straight ahead."

"Take a deep, slow, deliberate breath through your nose, and fill your lungs as deeply as you can. Good, now pause. Breathe out through your nose as slowly and as deeply as you can, emptying all of the air from your lungs. Very good, now pause". (One completed breath cycle) "Inhale slowly and deeply. That's good, now pause. Exhale slowly and deeply. Good, now pause". (Two completed breath cycles.)

"Inhale slowly and deeply. Good, now pause. Exhale slowly and deeply. Good, now pause. (Three completed breath cycles.)"

"Now breath in as deeply as you can, through your nose. Hold your breath and squeeze the muscles tight in your anus and genitals, as if you need to go to the toilet. Now swallow keeping your throat closed and continue to hold your breath, do not release your breath until I tell you to".

At this point you can then shift the Assemblage Point to a new location.

Clinical Shifting

Shifting and realignment of pathological Assemblage Point locations must be backed up with professional patient management and should only be carried out by professionally qualified personnel. Clinical shifting associated with physiological and psychological health problems requires two experienced professionals. At least one of them should be qualified in the psychological field. One is required to locate the Assemblage Point and the second to do the shifting. Each will double-check the other's work. However if a trained practitioner is unavailable, and one is very confident that the location of a patient's Assemblage Point is in a detrimental location, then one should not be discouraged from attempting to correct it. The sliding method is not normally used, except perhaps for patients with breathing problems, heart problems or a pacemaker. With the following method, the patient can keep his clothes on. Instead of sliding the Assemblage Point towards the centre, shifting is done in several stages or short steps (5.8.). The rear location or pivot point is dislodged with a firm push to the patient's back. Normally, the palm of the right hand is used to deliberately slap or shove the pivot point. Shifts of a short distance require only one stage and two pushes. Large distances may require three stages and four pushes to shift it to the centre. The rest of the procedure is the same as for the sliding method above. This method of shifting has another advantage over the previous method, the Assemblage can be also shifted in depth. The depth is determined by the

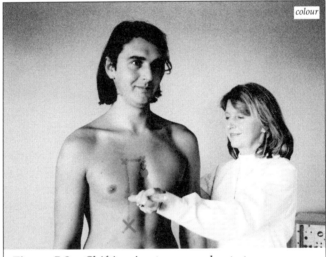

Figure 5.8   Shifting in stages or short steps.

force of the shift (this is explained further in the Postscript at the end of this book).

1. Use two small adhesive labels to mark the front and rear Assemblage Point locations. Plan the number of stages you will use to move the Assemblage Point to the centre - normally not more than four.

2. Use your left hand to position the crystal on the first stage. Firmly

instruct the patient through Steps 2 to 6 as in the Sliding Shift above and by reading out loud them the notes in: "How to Instruct Your Subject Or Patient", above. When the patient is holding his breath and the sphincter muscles and his throat are closed, give a firm push or slap to the Assemblage Point rear location with the heel of your right hand. The Assemblage Point will jump and relocate at the crystal. Note: large strong willed subjects often require a firm shove or slap or thump with the palm of your right hand on the rear pivot point to dislodge it.

3. Rapidly move the crystal to stage 2 and again shove or slap the rear location. Long shifts may require a third stage, so push the rear location again to shift the Assemblage Point to the third stage. The patient must continue to hold his breath throughout. You only have a few seconds before he will need to breathe again, therefore you must be practiced and swift.

4. When you arrive with the crystal at the centre give a final firm push between the shoulder blades and remove the crystal from the patient's chest with a half twist. Simultaneously, using the four fingers of your now free right hand, tap the patient lightly on the head and instruct him to breath normally.

Allow the patient a few moments to rest. Always re-check the Assemblage Point location, making sure that it has not been left behind at one of the stages. If necessary, repeat the procedure. After the shift, get the patient to lie down, breathe freely and relax for about fifteen minutes. This helps to "fix" the new location.

As mentioned previously, psychiatric patients suffering from schizophrenia or manic depression can often have an "energy shadow" and "split" Assemblage Point locations. The dominant Assemblage Point must be located and shifted to the secondary split or shadow location. Both are then picked up with the crystal and shifted to the centre. Examples are shown in figure 5.7. Splits and shadows are not easy to deal with and considerable experience in locating and shifting Assemblage Points is required to be effective.

Dropped rear locations (figure 5.1) adversely affect muscular co-ordination and mobility. Several patients on long-term drug management programmes have attended for treatment with Parkinson type symptoms. Their rear location was below the shoulder blades. In each case, shifting their Assemblage Point up to the centre stopped the symptoms. This suggests that rear brain energy levels and activity may fall as the Assemblage Point drops towards the navel.

Confirming The New Location

It is helpful to familiarise the patient with his original Assemblage Point location and the new position after the shift. Touching or pushing the spot with your finger will cause the skin to redden more than skin elsewhere on the chest. The spot is often tender, sore or uncomfortable. Pushing it causes the subject a feeling of slight unease. The feeling passes deep into the chest, often right through to the shoulder blade. Helping patients to take conscious note of the new position will allow them to keep track of their Assemblage Point, and arrange to have it corrected in the future, should it become necessary.

The Period Between Assemblage Point Shifts

For personal and group development purposes the Assemblage Point can be shifted monthly. It can also be centralised before important meetings or after stressful events. Sports and other team activities can benefit if all members are given the same alignment.

Patients should be re-assessed and their Assemblage Point corrected within ten to fourteen days of their first shift. It should then be corrected monthly until their location stabilises. Patients taking antidepressants, tranquillisers or other types of drugs, may require lower dosages or a different drug treatment after realignment. Patients withdrawing from non-prescribed drugs or alcohol may require daily shifting for one week or more until their biological and nervous systems adjust and stabilise.

Who Can And Cannot Shift Assemblage Points

Not everyone has the ability or propensity to acquire the skills for locating and shifting Assemblage Points. Their ability will depend upon factors such as physical stature, self determination, intelligence, sensitivity and personality. People who use strong medications, excessive alcohol, are suffering from poor health or are physically or mentally handicapped, generally speaking, will not be able to locate or shift Assemblage Points. The following guidelines are helpful in predetermining suitability for the task.

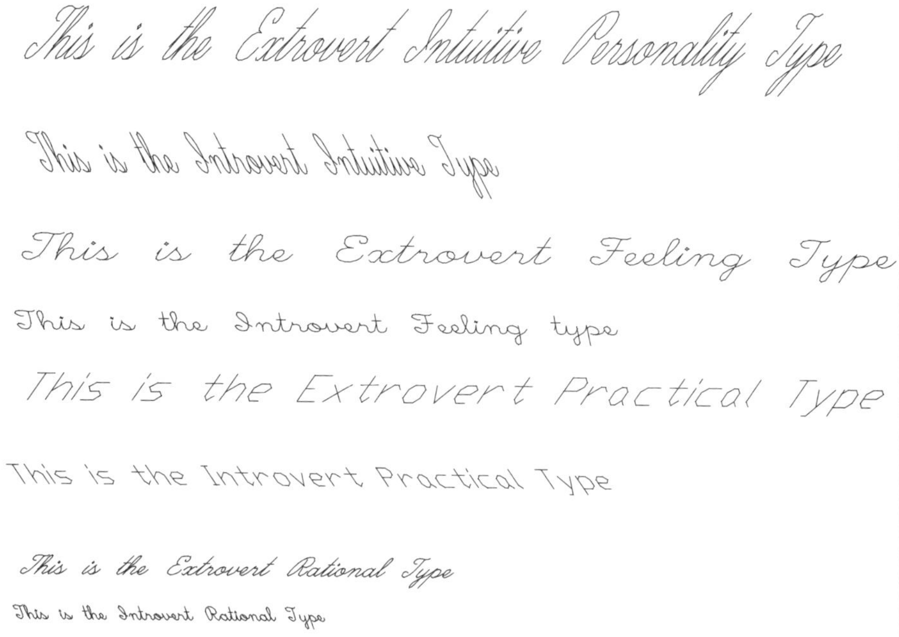

This is the Extrovert Intuitive Personality Type

This is the Introvert Intuitive Type

This is the Extrovert Feeling Type

This is the Introvert Feeling type

This is the Extrovert Practical Type

This is the Introvert Practical Type

This is the Extrovert Rational Type

This is the Introvert Rational Type

Figure 5.9   Computer simulated handwriting for different personality types (Reduced in size by 70%).

1. Extrovert intuitive personality types generally are able to locate and shift Assemblage Points. However, only a very small percentage of the population are of this type.

2. Introvert intuitive personality types can probably locate Assemblage Points but may experience some difficulties at first with shifting them.

3. Extrovert feeling personality types generally are able to locate and shift Assemblage Points.

4. Introvert feeling personality types can usually locate Assemblage Points but perhaps will experience some difficulties with shifting them.

5. Extrovert practical personality types will have problems in locating and shifting. Practical personalities are usually physically hardier than intuitive and feeling types; being less sensitive, they experience difficulties in detecting the location. However, they generally have the physical strength to shift Assemblage Points.

6. Introvert practical personalities will not generally be disposed to the work of locating and shifting Assemblage Points.

7. Extrovert and introvert rational personalities also will not be disposed to working with Assemblage Points. Generally rational personality types, rationalise everything which comes their way. For the rational type, thinking is more important than feeling. Therefore they may not have developed the physical concentration and sensitivity skills required.

The main qualities for working with Assemblage Points are: an intuitive or feeling type of person of medium height and weight, relatively strong and fit, with high ethical values, confidence, enthusiasm, strong intent and will power; above average intelligence and a considerate and understanding personality.

A person's personality qualities are reflected in their handwriting. In graphology one learns that feeling personality types have round circular wave forms in their handwriting, intuitive types reach up high and practical types are angular. Figure 5.9 is a useful computer simulation or approximation of the styles of handwriting for each personality type and gives some idea of the style, size and form.

When it comes to locating Assemblage Points, women are usually far superior to men. Women tend to be more intuitive and they are better equipped at detecting shadows and split locations. On the other hand, men have superior physical strength and are more familiar with giving instructions with authority. Consequently, men are better at shifting and correcting the Assemblage Point location, especially when it comes to complex procedures for joining split Assemblage Point locations. Many women may feel slightly intimidated attempting to correct the alignment of a large male patient. In practice, the best working combination is a male and female partnership.

Stick to The Procedures And Rules

The above procedures should be rigidly adhered to. They have been developed over many years of clinical experience and they take into account various unseen factors or circumstances which are not obvious to the novice. For example, it is difficult to locate the Assemblage Point if the practitioner turns up for work not feeling well, stressed or emotionally upset, jet lagged, hung over or under the influence of alcohol or depressive drugs. Under these circumstances, a second practitioner is indispensable.

Sticking to the rules is essential for consistent and reliable results. Shifting Assemblage Points is a skill and requires continual practice. Adhering to the procedures right from the beginning is the only way to prevent the development of poor or ineffective techniques.

Contra-indications And Limitations

The following case illustrates a typical situation where it is inappropriate to shift the Assemblage Point by the methods outlined above. Shifting the patient's Assemblage Point may well help her depression for a while, but it will not resolve the cause of the patient's depression.

Case 26. Partial Paralysis and Depression following Hip Replacement Surgery

Mrs J. L., aged 58. September 1996. Some 3 years previously, this charming and kind lady underwent replacement surgery to her right hip. At that time, her spinal nerve was injured by the epidural injection used. This resulted in impaired mobility of her left leg and foot, together with a cold and numb sensation. She was reporting a foot infection, with no pain or any other sensation. Her foot was cold to the touch.

J. L.'s G.P. had been treating her infection with antibiotics for 9 months without improvement. She had developed digestion and gastric problems due to the antibiotics. She was obviously debilitated and depressed, although she retained her sense of humour. She was told, antibiotics or not, that the circulation in her foot had to be stimulated for the infection to clear up. Without adequate blood flow, neither the body's defence mechanisms nor the antibiotics would reach the infected tissue. Her Assemblage Point had dropped, reflecting her general low state of health.

It was inappropriate to shift J.L.'s Assemblage Point. She was given "bliss therapy", using violet lamps and blue sapphire to each side of her head. The gems were pulsed at Theta brain-wave frequencies to induce a deep state of relaxation. While this was going on, her foot was energised with rubies and diamond to increase the heat and circulation. Finally, her thymus gland (controlling the immune defence system) was energised with a mixture of gems, at a stimulating frequency. At this point her face flushed with colour and she became very talkative. Afterwards, her Assemblage Point was checked; it had moved 8 cm upwards, just slightly to the right of the central position. Her foot infection cleared with a single treatment and she required no further therapy.

The Assemblage Point diagnosis and correcting methods were first researched and developed in the nineteen eighties. Since then knowledge and experience have progressed the techniques to the point where they are much more sophisticated. Today these methods are not often applied or used on patients; much more subtle methods of shifting and correcting patients' Assemblage Points having been developed. However, it is necessary in the first instance, as with any subject which one wishes to master in depth and integrate with one's existing skills, to learn and practice the techniques above as they will give a firm foundation of training. Until the Assemblage Point can be reliably detected by scientific electronic instrumentation or special photographic equipment, the only reliable method for locating it is by using the methods in the previous chapter.

In old age, the energy body's vibrational rate slows with the decrease in biological energy. The Assemblage Point falls naturally towards the "gap" as death approaches. With old or frail patients, it is neither practical nor advisable to shift their Assemblage Point. In any event very infirm patients are not able to co-operate in the first place, therefore the above outlined procedures are useless as they cannot be applied.

One very important point to observe is the patient's chronic psychological level. As the Assemblage Point central locations increase assertiveness, shifting the Assemblage Point of patients who have had a unsatisfactory psychological approach to life (for example, being generally angry or covertly hostile throughout life) may encourage the patients to use their newly acquired assertiveness unpleasantly. This type of patient can be difficult. Direct honesty is the best way to help them.

Shifting the Assemblage Point with Energy Medicine

The Assemblage Point can be shifted by more subtle and pleasurable means. Assemblage Points move around in trance and dream states of consciousness. The dominant brain frequency in trance and dreaming states is Theta (i.e., 3.2-7.8 Hz). Theta states of consciousness can be extremely pleasant. Slow Theta brain waves unite both halves of the brain. They are especially beneficial for de-stressing and physical healing. Most people experience Theta states during their night's sleep. These are dreamy, pleasurable states of semi-consciousness.

Electronic gem lamp therapy can induce Theta states of consciousness. The procedure is coined "bliss therapy" and it is often used to "fix" the patient's Assemblage Point after a manual shift. This procedure can be seen in Figure 5.10. Blue sapphire emits a soft, pleasurable, calming energy. It is used in two violet filtered lamps. Sometimes diamonds are added to the sapphires. The lamps are directed at each side of the head. The patient is kept warm, fully relaxed and comfortable in quiet surroundings. The sapphires are electronically pulsed at 3.3 Hz. Most patients will quickly enter a dream state of consciousness. The heart beat and blood pressure will fall and stabilise. This treatment induces pleasurable bodily sensations. The lamps are adjusted to balance the patient's energy field and alignment. Maximum body and mind

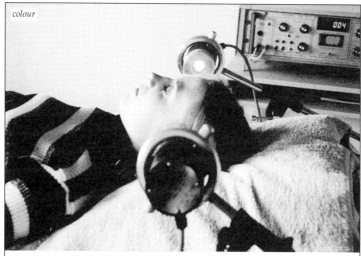

Figure 5.10 Energising the brain to adjust the Assemblage Point Location.

integration occurs with the central location.

Where disease and illness is responsible for Assemblage Point misalignment the situation can be addressed with energy medicine. The patient's blood, glands and organs can be energised and balanced using various energy medicine procedures. Energising underactive or calming overactive glands and organs can promote a profound feeling of well-being. This will be accompanied by higher levels of physical and mental energy. Targeting energy medicine therapies will shift the Assemblage Point location and raise the vibrational frequency of the energy body, which is reflected in the patient's attitude and complexion. Energy medicine is now the preferred method of shifting the Assemblage Point. Numerous case studies and energy medical therapies for shifting the Assemblage Point are discussed in Chapter Seven. However, the Assemblage Point location procedures are, at the moment, indispensable for accurate diagnosis.

chapter 6

THE ELECTRONIC DOCTOR

The average person has been thoroughly conditioned to believe that their body is a chemical universe. Disease is caused by an invasion of bacteria or a virus, or some malfunction of the body. Most people believe that medication, to be effective, must be a special chemical designed to kill, correct or compensate for the disease. Chapter Five has demonstrated the use of a large quartz crystal for the purpose of arresting or capturing the patient's Assemblage Point. The practitioner uses the quartz crystal to capture the patient's Assemblage Point in order to be able to move it to a new location to improve their patient's health. For the average person this simple procedure must seem astonishing, or even unbelievable.

The disbelief concerning the medical power of gem stones held by many western doctors and the western public is groundless and irrational. It seems most likely that it is due to an ignorance of historical medical practices and the preparation of medicines used by physicians from other cultures. This is despite the fact that historical records provide us with thousands of examples of medical preparations of gem stones which have been used successfully for millennia. If they worked successfully in the past, why are they not used today by the Health Services?

Electronic engineers and scientists have known about the special properties of crystalline minerals for more than a century now. Quartz crystals are formed from silicon dioxide. Crystalline minerals are used extensively throughout the electronic and scientific industries; for example silicon chips and silicon transistors. Outlined in the previous chapter is a method of stimulating or exciting the piezoelectric properties of a quartz crystal by squeezing it with your hand to increase the activity and energy output from the crystal's pointed end. The average person experiencing the energy emitted from the crystal's point will find it incredible. However, it will be of no surprise to a scientist or electronic engineer.

The piezoelectric properties of quartz convert mechanical vibrations or kinetic energy into electrical signals, and quartz crystals have been used for decades by electronic manufacturers. Microphones, record players, watches, clocks, radio and television sets, transmitters, medical ultrasonic transducers and computers are just some of the thousands of manufactured items that depend on the natural electrical properties of quartz. Another aspect of quartz is that it will resonate at a specific frequency which is related to the physical size of the crystal. There are many hundreds of different crystalline minerals which have strange and useful medical scientific properties.

The Ancient Origins of Energy Medicine

In the twelfth century a Spanish King, Alfonso X el Sabio (The Learned), translated and recorded in a lapidary the properties of at least three hundred and sixty different stones and gems (see Figure 6.1). The original book is held in a magnificent library on a hill, just outside Madrid. Today, there are only three known nineteenth century lithographic copies in the world. These belong to private collectors and one is owned by this author. This fabulous book records the extraordinary properties of the gems listed. Many of the gems have Arabic names and it is said that the book is a compilation of Arabic scrolls and parchments. No doubt the medical knowledge that this book contains was conveyed along the old silk routes, together with the gem medicines and stones themselves. The book is a compilation of both medical and astrological sciences. It is supported with numerous brilliantly coloured and skillfully painted colour plates. There is a startling beauty in the pages, with pictures of the twelve astrological signs of the zodiac, as well as depictions of medieval life surrounding the mining and preparation of gems and minerals.

There are many examples of the medical properties, preparations and administration of gem medicines. Of diamond, King Alfonso's book states: *". . .if a little of this powder is given to a man suffering from a stone in the bladder, the stone is immediately destroyed and the patient is cured."* Two further examples are: *". . . diamond is cold and dry in nature and its powers are such that those who carry it are able to do anything that demands bravery and daring." and ". . . take a small splinter of diamond and fix it to a thin piece of iron and apply it to a man who suffers from a stone in the genital parts in such a way that, when the diamond comes into contact with the diseased part, the stone is immediately broken up."*

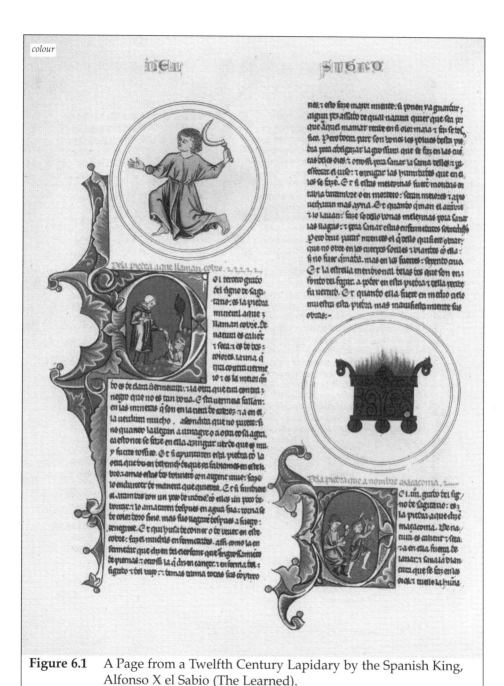

Figure 6.1   A Page from a Twelfth Century Lapidary by the Spanish King, Alfonso X el Sabio (The Learned).

The more contemporary names for stones of the genital parts could be tumours and cysts. Another example of the power of gem stones is:

"There is a gem stone of sleep. . . . This stone is prized by physicians and surgeons because it brings a calm and restful slumber, after which the patient awakens clear minded and refreshed in body; . . . This powerful stone must be handled with great caution and taken only in small quantities. One single drachma is sufficient to bring on uninterrupted sleep for three whole days and nights.[1]

The powders are microscopic crystals and, unlike all chemical medications, they do not dissolve in water and are not absorbed by the body but pass though and are eliminated by the digestive track. These medicines are extremely effective and influence biological energy at the atomic level by dielectric resonance (inductance and capacitance) with the valence electrons of atoms which make up living cells. The blood circulating around the stomach and intestines is energised with the specific frequencies dictated by the colour of the gem powder. The blood then transports the energy to other parts of the body. It could be said that gem medicines were **the first truly non-chemical energy medicine to be used.**

Concerning ruby this book advises:

". . . when ruby is reduced to powder, it is mixed for remedies for weakness of the heart, and can be used effectively to cure sores and break up blood clots".

Today, Indian practitioners use the paste of ruby for these and many other ailments. Such is the power of ruby that the lasers used in hospitals are powered by a long ruby crystal rod. Lasers are used in surgery for the cutting and removal of unwanted, infected skin and tissue and various other medical procedures. The surgeon's laser beam can attain temperatures many times hotter than the surface of the Sun. The following story from India demonstrates the power of large rubies when worn close to the skin.

". . . a certain businessman from Bombay purchased a very large ruby. He had it set in a ring to serve as a charm to promote his business. After three months he began to feel ill, having a constantly high temperature. When he visited his doctor, he was prescribed drugs to reduce his temperature. He eventually collapsed, was admitted to hospital unconscious and was given stimulants which helped him to recover consciousness, but his legs were paralysed. For the next two years, he followed all kinds of treatments which only resulted in profound depression and

apathy. Not only had he lost his health but his business had to be sold. Finally, he consulted a homoeopath who prescribed him a number of remedies. The homoeopath experienced conflicting results, the patient's temperature refused to come down. Then one day, the homoeopath noticed the huge ruby on his finger. After removing the ring, the man gradually began to recover."

The energy rays emitted from rubies are hot and increase the metabolic rate. If a long rod of man made ruby, such as is used in lasers, is held firmly in the hand and exposed to sunlight, the person holding the ruby rod will soon start to experience the effects. Ruby converts sunlight to a hot red frequency.

The Sun is our prime source of biological energy or "life force". If we place a healthy plant in the dark, keep it warm, and give it water and nutrients, it will soon die. Life is unsustainable without the vital energy of the light.

According to Dr Richard Hobday's book, *The Healing Sun*, research has associated a number of diseases with insufficient vitamin D. Exposure to the sun increases the body's levels of vitamin D. For people who live in the northern hemispheres where there are low levels of sunlight, there is a greater chance of becoming ill. This is a fairly obvious fact, known to all of us who live close to the Earth's north pole. However, some of the conditions which are associated with the sunlight deficiency mentioned in his

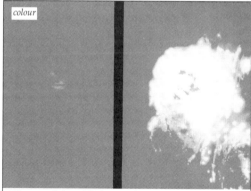

Figure 6.2   Kirlian photograph comparing processed (left) and natural (right) foods.

book are very serious; they include: breast cancer, colon cancer, diabetes, elevated blood pressure, heart disease, multiple sclerosis, ovarian cancer, osteomalacia, osteoporosis, prostate cancer, psoriasis, rickets, seasonal affective disorders, tooth decay and tuberculosis. Dr Hobday's book contains very useful information on safe ways to improve health by exposure to the sun.

Kirlian photography shows clearly the biological energy, or "life force", in humans, animals, living fruit, vegetables, seeds, and so on. The "life energy" can be seen as an aura extending as lines of force from the object. Kirlian photographs of processed foods demonstrate that they contain little or no biological energy (Figure 6.2).

British law insists that our processed food containers state the chemical contents. Fat, protein, vitamins, minerals, colouring and calories are listed – all wholesome and complete, except that there is no mention of the "life force" contents. Kirlian photography has, to some extent, demonstrated that "junk food" diets deplete a person's biological energy. One could deduce from this that digesting and assimilating "junk" foods uses up more biological energy than the foods themselves provide. Quite obviously, these two photographs also demonstrate that eating fresh food which is still alive will increase our biological energy. Fresh food has the energy of the sun trapped in it, it is fully charged with the invisible energy which can be seen with the aid of kirlian photography.

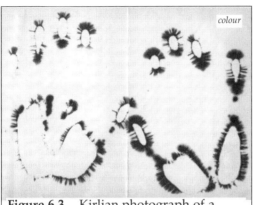

Figure 6.3   Kirlian photograph of a normal left hand and a diamond ray energised right hand.

With death, our vital "life force" departs and the organic body becomes overrun with bacteria while it decays. It is the biological energy or life force which protects living cells from invasion. If our biological energy reserves become low, we are more susceptible to illness. Various opportunist bacteria and viruses are likely to invade us. Under these circumstances, we are forced to rest and take wholesome foods until our immune defence system has cleaned up the invaders. The "life force" within us is finite, otherwise we would not become ill or die. Young people have an excess of biological energy and find it hard to comprehend these truths. With increasing age, sensible adults take care to conserve their energy and adjust their habits and behaviour accordingly.

Many oriental doctors evaluate their patients' "life force" and its quality. They make adjustments to the patients' biological energy with acupuncture, herbs and diet, change the quality and increase their patients' biological energy, and they use medicines prepared from

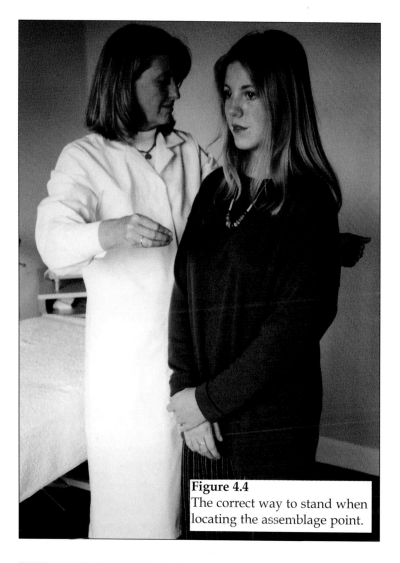

Figure 4.4
The correct way to stand when locating the assemblage point.

Figure 4.5
How to 'form your hands' for locating the assemblage point.

Figure 4.6
How to 'form your hands' for locating the assemblage point.

Figure 5.2.
Assemblage Point shifting
quartz crystals.

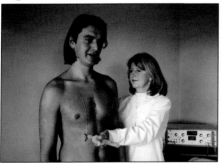

Figure 5.5
Using the 'sliding shift'
from a low location.

Figure 5.4.
Checking the crystal
for energy activity.

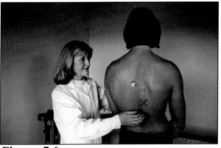

Figure 5.6
Using the right hand to raise the
rear 'pivot point' location.

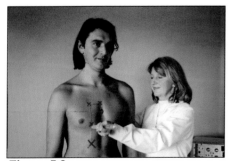

Figure 5.8
Shifting in stages or short steps.

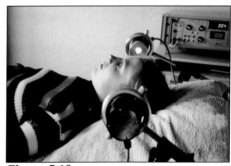

Figure 5.10
Energising the brain to adjust the
Assemblage Point Location.

Figure 6.1
A Page from a twelfth century gem stone medical book
by the Spanish King, Alfonso X el Sabio (The Learned).

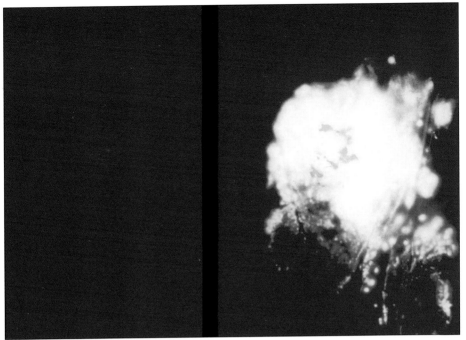

Figure 6.2
Kirlian photograph comparing processed (left) and natural foods (right).

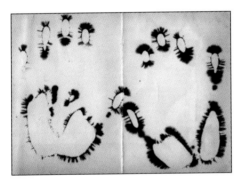

Figure 6.3
Kirlian photograph of a normal left hand and a diamond ray energised right hand.

Figure 6.4
Ruby rays increase skin circulation and skin temperature.

Figure 6.5
Emerald rays reduce circulation and skin temperature

Figure 7.1
Treatment for sciatica
and back pains.

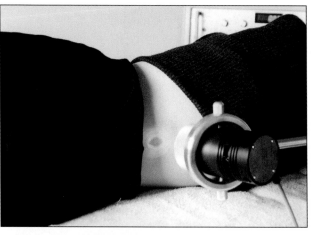

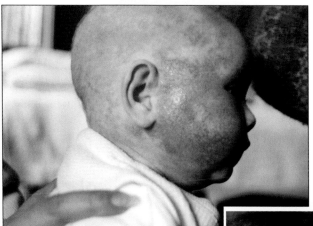

Figure 7.2
Baby J with
contact eczema.

Figure 7.3
J's eye infection is given
yellow sapphire rays.

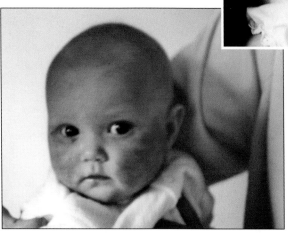

Figure 7.4
J after two full treatments
of emerald and sapphire.

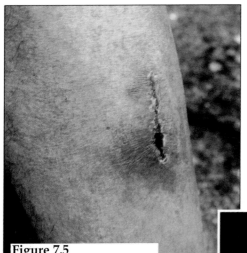

Figure 7.5
Infected leg injury with dermatitis complications.

Figure 7.6
Treatment of the infected injury with yellow sapphire rays.

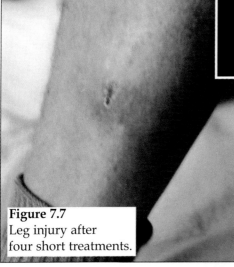

Figure 7.7
Leg injury after four short treatments.

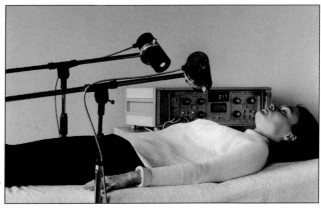

Figure 7.8
Treatment for asthma.

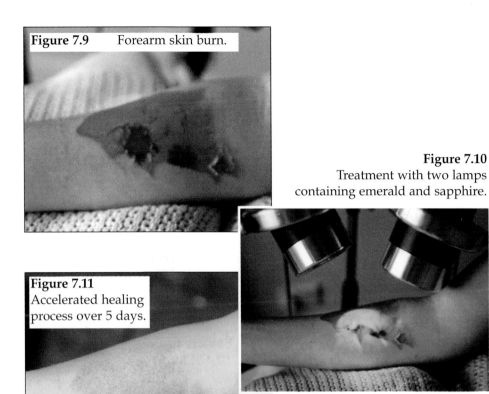

Figure 7.9 Forearm skin burn.

Figure 7.10
Treatment with two lamps
containing emerald and sapphire.

Figure 7.11
Accelerated healing
process over 5 days.

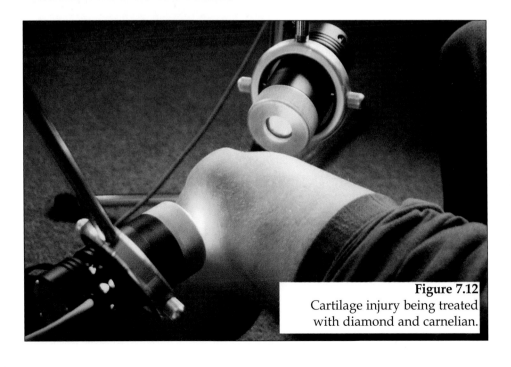

Figure 7.12
Cartilage injury being treated
with diamond and carnelian.

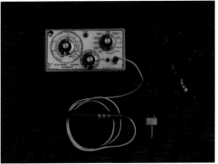

Figure A3.1
A Battery powered hand held
gem therapy instrument
constructed in first built in1985.

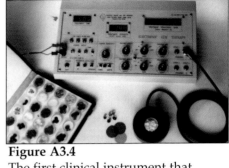

Figure A3.4
The first clinical instrument that
combined the use of colour light and
electronically excited gem stones.

Figure A3.5
Irritable bowel syndrom under
treatment with wooden lamps.

appendix 3

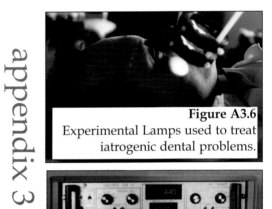

Figure A3.6
Experimental Lamps used to treat
iatrogenic dental problems.

Figure A3.8
A dual channel manual
instrument, Caduceus Lux II.

Figure A3.7
An instrument with automatic
treatment selection, Caduceus Lux III.

Figure A3.9
High powered lamps
machined from metal.

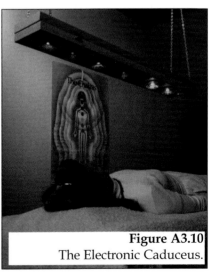

Figure A3.10
The Electronic Caduceus.

precious gem stones. Like the Sun, gem stones are a powerful source of pure biological energy and their colour dictates the quality of the biological energy they emit. Figure 6.3. is a Kirlian photograph of a pair of hands which demonstrates the biological power of diamond. The right hand has been energised for a few minutes with an electronic gem therapy lamp containing diamonds. The additional biological energy induced by the diamond lamp can clearly be seen as a greater number of outward radiating black lines.

The Medical Power of Precious Gems

There are hundreds of famous stories divulging the medical powers of diamonds and other types of gems. The infamous Koh-i-noor diamond is today owned by the British Royal Family. It was presented to Queen Victoria in 1850 and weighed 193 carats. Years later it was re-cut and now weighs a priceless 106.5 carats. The water in which the great Koh-i-noor diamond was steeped in when in India was said to heal every kind of sickness.

Many ancient and modern books on medical books have laid down methods and procedures for the preparation and administration of gem stone medicines, which are today still strictly followed. For thousands of years physicians have used the ashes and powders of precious stones for medicinal purposes. Even today, these ashes and powders are very commonly used by Indian and Tibetan physicians for the treatment of critical diseases. All the precious stones, such as diamond, ruby, pearl, coral and yellow, white and blue sapphires, are used for this purpose. The procedures for the preparation of ashes and powders is time consuming and complicated. Gem medicine preparations are available from Indian and Tibetan pharmacies. Generally, they are mixed with herbs and other medical substrates or adjuncts. The mixing of the gem paste or ash amplifies the effects of adjuncts, such as herbs. The adjuncts are chosen for their additional beneficial effects for the disease being treated. Many prescriptions can contain up to thirty different ingredients with combinations of gem powders, minerals, metals and herbs and fruit or vegetable concentrates. They are the most expensive and most effective medicines available in their pharmacies. These gem ashes and powders are used because they have immense power for curing diseases and should be handled and administered with the same precautions as strong drugs. This information is included for the benefit of the reader's understanding of the depth and scope of this ancient medical science. The

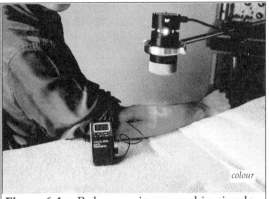

Figure 6.4. Ruby rays increase skin circulation and skin temperature.

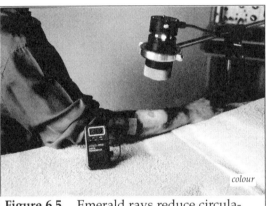

Figure 6.5 Emerald rays reduce circulation and skin temperature.

following preparations are very potent medications and should only be prescribed and administered by a doctor trained in their use.

Gem stones emit concentrated rays of strong, pure energy. The energy emitted is specific to the colour of the gem used. Ruby emits hot, red rays and is used to treat diseases arising from cold and dampness of the body Tibetan. and Indian doctors employ the heat of ruby to treat problems like varicose ulcers, low blood pressure, thrombosis, low libido, constipation and anaemia - these are all cold diseases. Ruby raises the skin and body temperature, increases the metabolic rate and circulation and also increases muscle tension (figure 6.4.). Ruby is beneficial for patients with a large, heavy body type, and a slow, cold physiological disposition. Ruby is contraindicated and is not for the agile, quick, and hot tempered physiological types.

In contrast, emerald emits cold, green rays and is used to treat diseases arising from too much heat, such as burns, contusions, anorexia, diarrhoea, irritable bowel syndrome, stomach ulcers, cystitis and eczema. The green rays of emerald lower skin and body temperature, reduce libido, slow the metabolic rate and circulation, relax muscle tension and increase the patient's body weight (figure 6.5.).

The effects of ruby and emerald can be scientifically confirmed by monitoring a patient's pulse or by using a thermometer or a blood pressure monitor before and after treatment with gem medicines.

Wealthy Indians and Arabs often wear medicine rings set with very large high quality gem stones. The rings are open behind the gem so that the light passing through shines onto the skin. The rings are changed periodically according to the advice and instructions of their astrologer or doctor. Some Indian doctors work in conjunction with an astrologer and take into account the effects of the planets on the health of their patients. They prescribe gems to be worn for the prevention and treatment of disease as well as disease that may arise for the patient in the future. Each planet reflects a different coloured light from the Sun, which has an influence on biological organisms on Earth. Anyone who has any doubt about this should reconsider the moon's effect on women's menstrual cycles. Specific gem stones are assigned to each of the planets and are used to amplify their beneficial effects and counteract the harmful effects of particular planetary configurations. In other words, gem stones are worn to balance the background cosmic energy radiated to Earth. This energy changes with the seasons and the ever changing positions of the planets. Medicine rings take time to be effective and high street decorative jewellery, which usually contains only small gems, will have no effect. Only large, clear gem stones of good quality are effective for medical purposes.

Powdered Gem Medicines of Tibet

European, Tibetan and Indian gem medicines are prepared by crushing the gems into a fine paste or burning them to ash. These are mixed with selected herbs and oils, which are then made up into pills and balms. For some diseases, precious metals such as gold and silver are included. These medical preparations are exceptionally strong and effective.

Ancient Medical Preparations of Diamond

The biological effects of diamond are: stimulating, invigorating, clarifying, antiseptic and antidepressant. Diamond is the hardest of all gemstones. It should never be used orally in the form of ground paste. Only the ashes or oxide are used for internal use. If diamond particles get into the stomach, they can cause fatal internal bleeding. Therefore, diamond is purified very carefully. In India, there are many traditional methods of preparing diamond oxide.

Purified pieces of diamond are placed in an iron crucible and heated until the crucible and diamonds are red hot. Then the diamonds are submersed in rose water. This process is repeated, many, many times to break up the crystal structure. The diamond pieces are powdered with rose water by grinding in a mortar. A tablet of the resulting paste is made and dried. This tablet is placed in a crucible made of two clay pots, which are then sealed together with cloth strips soaked in clay. This is fired in a potter's kiln, until it is red hot. This process is repeated at least twelve times and each time the diamonds are ground in rose water and re-sealed in the crucible and fired again.

After the firings the diamond oxide is ground in various plant extracts, re-sealed in the clay crucible and is fired again. This process is repeated until the oxide becomes soft, red ashes which are ready for medicinal purposes. It can take up to thirty firings to reduce diamonds to their oxide.

DOSAGE: 3 to 6 milligrams are mixed with various combinations of medicinal herbs chosen to suit the symptoms being treated. A typical Indian example is:

"For weakness caused by a loss of semen (impotency) the paste should be used with honey, and then the patient should drink milk boiled with dates with a pinch of fine-ground saffron".

Oxide of diamond is prescribed for tuberculosis, insane imaginations, dropsy, diabetes, ulcers in the anus, anaemia, inflammations etc.. It prolongs life and brings a radiance of good health to the face. If the ashes of diamond, combined with certain other adjuncts, are administered to a dying man, it is said that it immediately brings back consciousness and activity in his body and saves his life. The Indian medicine states that: "diamond by increasing and thickening the semen enhances virility in a man". By neutralising the ill effects of excess of wind, bile and phlegm, diamond is believed to have the power of curing all kinds of diseases and disorders. The diamond is said to contain six different medical powers which are considered to have great therapeutic value. Diamond ash bestows new life to those who have been deprived of all the joys of life due to lack or loss of sexual potency. It is useful in all kinds of disorders created by aggravated wind, bile, or mucus, disorders caused by fatness, obesity, cholesterol, chronic diarrhoea, stomach disorders, chronic dysentery, and viral infections. Diamond oxide provides life force. It is useful for epilepsy, paralysis, insanity, hernia, premature old age, sterility, and uterine diseases. It is also prescribed for general debility, weakness of the mind, diabetes, and jaundice. It makes the body strong and aids longevity. It is used in angina pectoralis, poor circulation, anaemia, weakness of nerves, poor vision, blindness, menstrual disorders, leukorrhoea and burning sensations within the body.

Ancient Medical Preparations of Blue Sapphire

The biological effects of blue sapphire are cool, tranquillizing, soothing, analgesic, sedative and antispasmodic. The smooth fine ash powder is taken with honey, cream of milk, the juice of ginger or six betel nut leaves. This preparation cures all kinds of fevers, epilepsy, brain weakness, insanity and hiccups. The ashes of blue sapphire are used for diseases like gout, rheumatism, stiffness of the joints, colic pains, neurotic pains and fainting etc.

Blue Sapphire Oxide
A mixture of purified blue sapphire powder with equal proportions of sulphur is ground in a mortar for twelve hours with rose water. Then the resulting paste is made into a tablet and dried. The tablet is placed in a crucible made of two clay pots, sealed together with cloth strips soaked in clay. This is fired in a potter's kiln. This process is repeated twelve times before the oxide is ready for medicinal purposes.

DOSAGE: 50 to 100 milligrams twice a day with one tsp. honey, or sugar and butter, or powdered sugar.

Blue Sapphire Paste
Purified blue sapphire should be finely powdered and sieved through a piece of fine cloth. The resulting fine dust is further ground in a mortar with rose water for fifteen days. When the paste is fine and smooth, it should be dried. Then the process should be repeated and ground into an even finer powder.

DOSAGE: 50 to 100 milligrams twice a day with honey or cream, or ginger juice and powdered sugar, or betel juice and powdered sugar.

Blue sapphire oxide or powder is a powerful remedy and is prescribed by Indian and Tibetan doctors. Blue sapphire paste, mixed with beneficial herbs, can also be made into small pills and dried. These are given for chronic fever, asthma, mucus, haemorrhoids, epilepsy, hysteria, neuritis, pain or stiffness in the joints, insanity, weakness of the mind and brain, all nervous disorders, loss of memory, confusion, heart disease, tuberculosis, baldness, skin diseases, eczema, psoriasis, migraine, heartburn, gout, sciatica, rheumatism, colic pains, loss of appetite, swelling of the stomach and diseases of the urinary tract. It increases energy radiance and biological energy, but at a calm level.

Jewel pills made from gem powder have rejuvenating powers and are the most expensive of the medicines in the Tibetan pharmacopoeia. They are wrapped in silk, and cost about £1.00 each - a day's pay in Dharmsala. However, using crushed gem stones is rather wasteful and gem stone pills are too expensive to be widely available. Indian doctors prepare medicines from gem stones without destroying them in the process. Gem stones are placed inside a bottle of 95% ethyl alcohol. Nine bottles are used, each with a different gem stone and containing four or five cut and polished gems. The nine bottles are then placed in a box and the box is stored in a dark place for 3 months. The remedies are made by spraying blank homeopathic tablets with the alcohol from the bottles as required. Unlike pills made from gem powder, these types of preparations are completely safe, even if mis-prescribed. Unfortunately, gem energy medicine preparations do not have a long shelf-life because their energy is continually dissipating. They must be prepared freshly for the patient and used immediately.

WARNING: Do not ingest the powder or ash of gem stones, or take pills prepared from gem stone powder or metals, without expert medical advice

Gem Stones are Reservoirs of Pure Radiating Energy

The white light from the Sun has a broad spectrum, made up of seven bands of frequencies. These colour bands can be seen in a rainbow. Gem stones emit concentrated rays of pure colour. The light of the Sun or ordinary colour therapy lamps only just penetrate the skin, and their beneficial effect has to be carried deeper by the blood. When we stand in front of a coal fire, invisible, low frequency infra-red rays pass through the body. Infra-red creates the feeling of heat in the body by speeding up the electron activity inside the atoms of tissue and bone marrow as the rays pass through. All warm-blooded animals enjoy the input of energy from infra-red rays. Cold weather slows our vibrational rate, our muscles go tense, and we shiver, burning calories in order to generate heat. Infra-red rays raise our atomic vibrational rate and relax our endocrine system.

The concentrated rays of gems influence cellular activity at an atomic level where gross chemicals, such as herbs and drugs, cannot penetrate.

The beam of a hospital's ruby laser vapourises molecules on contact and can cut through almost any substance. Many crystalline materials can transmute energy from one level to another. Lasers are a dramatic example of the power of gem stones. Gem rays can pass through the body and influence cellular behaviour in a similar way to that of infra-red rays. The colour of the gem stone determines its effect on the living cells.

Natural Crystals or Polished Gem Stones?

Many people confuse New Age crystal therapy and electronic gem therapy, thinking them to be the same; they are not and do not really have any connection. The New Age use of crystals for healing is not backed up with medical research. It has largely been set up and promoted by numerous commercial enterprises in the United States of America, United Kingdom and elsewhere. Quartz crystals do not have much colour and, in this respect, their energy is non-specific. The energy of large crystals can be pleasant or irritating. Quartz crystals are not ascribed any specific medical properties in the textbooks of traditional Indian medicine and they do not have any medical track record. For this reason it is best to use the gems recommended by Indian doctors and to benefit from their store of expert knowledge and case studies, gathered over thousands of years. Gem stones have stable, inherent medical properties. These properties are independent of the person applying them. Therefore their use is consistent and repeatable. Faceted and polished gems give superior results when compared to natural crystals or geological samples. The more lustre and "fire" emitted by the gem, the more effective it is as medicine. Coloured glass and fake or paste gems have no power or medical use whatsoever.

Natural Healing Frequencies

A mother knows that rocking her crying child backwards and forwards once or twice each second encourages sleep. In fact, this rhythm is encouraging Delta brain waves. Massaging parts of the body slowly can induce Alpha, Theta and Delta brain frequencies, together with their corresponding moods. As far as promoting healing is concerned, sluggish cells, organs and glands which are vibrating too slowly will benefit from any method which will increase and unify their rhythm. Conversely, cells, organs and glands which are excited or stressed will benefit from any method which will reduce and unify their vibrational activity.

It is a scientific fact that the frequency of the brain's electrical activity is directly connected with health. In the case of anxiety and panic, the frequency of the electrical activity of the patient's brain will be in High Beta, i.e. above 25 Hz. These frequencies are reflected in excess adrenaline, muscular tension, and stress. Simply encouraging the patient's brain activity towards Alpha, or 8.5 Hz, will relieve the symptoms. Slow brain frequencies help the production of endorphins, which act like morphine to reduce pain and increase pleasure.

European, Indian and Tibetan Prescriptions

Listed below are some of the commonly used Indian and Tibetan gem stone prescriptions.

Ruby
Preparations from rubies are used for amenorrhoea, anaemia, constipation, debility, low blood pressure, hemiplegia, infantile paralysis, palpitations, paralysis, and syncope. The ruby induces biological energy which is hot, heating, drying, energising, and expanding, and is used for disorders arising from cold and dampness in the body.

Pearl
The powder of pearl is used for acidity, anger, asthma, bronchitis, chickenpox, conjunctivitis, delusions, dreams, fear, fever, haematuria, hay fever, high blood pressure, hysteria, influenza, dysmenorrhoea, oedema, pneumonia, rhinitis, tonsillitis, and whooping cough. Pearl's biological

energy is cooling, anti-allergic, harmonising, and moist. (Note: carnelian is often substituted for pearl.)

Coral
Red coral preparations are recommended for biliary colic, gall stones, haemorrhoids, hepatitis, jaundice, liver disease and warts. The yellow biological energy of coral is warm, enlivening and cleansing. (Note: citrine is often substituted for red coral.)

Emerald
Emerald and its various preparations are prescribed for anorexia, burns, cystitis, colitis, diarrhoea, eczema, heartburn, indigestion, inflammation, gastritis, shingles, stomach ulcers and vomiting. Emerald induces biological energy, which is cold, analgesic, unifying and solidifying. It is used for disorders arising from too much heat in the body.

Topaz
Indian topaz is yellow sapphire, which is employed for abscesses, adenoids, coughs, swollen glands, goitre, mumps, obesity, pancreatic disease and mouth ulcers. Yellow sapphire emits blue rays and it is cool, soft, satisfying and antiseptic.

Diamond
Diamond medications are prescribed for convulsions, depression, diabetes, eclampsia, epilepsy, leukorrhoea, menopausal symptoms, nephritis, spermatorrhoea, and sterility. Diamond induces biological energy which is stimulating, invigorating, clarifying, antiseptic and antidepressant.

Sapphire
Blue sapphire medications are prescribed for alopecia, backache, dandruff, dysmenorrhoea, earache, eczema, gout, headache, inflammation, laryngitis, lumbago, neuralgia, neuritis, orchitis, otorrhoea, Parkinson's disease, pericarditis, pharyngitis, psoriasis, and vertigo. Blue sapphire's biological energy is cool, tranquillizing, soothing, analgesic, sedative and antispasmodic.

Gem	Healing Energy Properties
Ruby	Hot, heating, drying, energising, expanding.
Pearl	Cooling, moist, and harmonising, anti-allergic.
Coral	Warm, enlivening, cleansing.
Emerald	Cold, unifying and solidifying, analgesic.
Topaz	Cool, soft, satisfying, antiseptic.
Diamond	Stimulating, invigorating, clarifying, antidepressant.
Sapphire	Cool, tranquillizing, soothing, analgesic, sedative.
Chrysoberyl	Soft, deep penetrating heat, drying, energising
Zircon	Coldest ray of all, used in cases of excess heat

These gems are used traditionally in medicines throughout India, Tibet, the Middle East and Europe. Their uses are backed up by an impressive number of case studies, recorded in medical and astrological textbooks.

Gem mixtures are much more effective than using a single gem. Often, in practice, remedies are prepared by mixing gems to combine their properties in one medication.

The Gem Stone Colour Code and Mixtures

To save time and space, gems are often referred to by their colour. This is particularly true when mixtures are called for in a patient's treatment. Note that pearl and red coral are substituted by carnelian and citrine.

Colour	Gem stone	True name	Substitute Gem
Infra-red	Cat's eye	Chrysoberyl	
Red	Ruby		
Orange	Pearl		Carnelian
Yellow	Red coral		Citrine
Green	Emerald		
Blue	Topaz	Yellow sapphire	
Indigo	Diamond		
Violet	Sapphire	Blue sapphire	
Ultra-violet	Onyx	Honey zircon	

Most Commonly Used Gem Mixtures

1) Sapphire, diamond, topaz and emerald.
2) Sapphire, diamond, topaz, emerald, coral, pearl and ruby.
3) Diamond, topaz, emerald and pearl.
4) Pearl, emerald, diamond and sapphire.
5) Ruby, coral, topaz and cat's eye.
6) Sapphire, diamond, topaz, emerald, coral, pearl, ruby, cat's eye and onyx.

Thus, for example, a medical preparation of mixture no.1, i.e. sapphire, diamond, topaz and emerald, would transmit all of the medical properties of the individual gem stones. Many other combinations are possible. For example, one commonly used mixture is diamond and carnelian. The properties of this mixture are: stimulating, invigorating and clarifying, antiseptic, antidepressant, cooling, moist, harmonising and anti-allergenic. This mixture is employed in the treatment of asthma, influenza, colds, bronchitis and circulatory problems.

Ancient physicians, using gem stones, minerals and herbs developed a powerful, efficient and versatile medical science. It seems that western orthodox medicine has ignored this in favour of developing chemical medications. When we read the ancient texts, the language and methods used in the past in comparison with today's standards are not scientific. Combining the traditional medical application of gem stones with modern scientific electronic technology produces astounding medical results and benefits for a wide range of diseases and symptoms. Electronic gem lamp therapies are a new precision scientific medical technology which have provided numerous major medical breakthroughs in the treatment of disease.

For the first time in medical history, we now have simple controllable energy medicine therapies which can precisely target the parts of the body which are diseased. We can increase and adjust the biological energy of any organ or gland which requires assistance. From this perspective chemical systemic medications and their side effects now look unscientific. Although currently there are not any medical drug therapies which can correct a patient's Assemblage Point location, electronic gem lamp therapy can be used to adjust its location.

chapter 7

REHABILITATING THE FREQUENCIES
AND ENERGIES OF SERIOUS DISEASES

During the nineteen eighties, many people were attending appointments to have their Assemblage Point checked and corrected. In these early days, the author was researching and developing the Assemblage Point correction techniques for psychological conditions, such as depression, anxiety, panic, lack of confidence or stress. These developments were very successful and Assemblage Point correction therapies started to attract patients with serious health problems. Some of these were suffering with common complaints, such as psoriasis, eczema or asthma. These patients were receiving orthodox and in some cases complementary medications or therapies and yet their symptoms persisted. Some of these patients were depressed or anxious. They were generally disillusioned with their medications and therapies. Some felt inadequate or guilty that their mental state was responsible for, or causing, their physical symptoms.

It very soon became apparent that diseases such as diabetes, asthma, eczema, psoriasis and many others had a profound effect on the location of the patient's Assemblage Point. It also became apparent that the patient's disease and, for example, an imbalance of their endocrine system, or a malfunction of their liver, spleen and so on, would be accompanied by various distressing psychological symptoms. Physical malfunction or imbalance of organs or the endocrine system was linked to the location of the patient's Assemblage Point. The patient's physical and psychological symptoms were also linked to the location of their Assemblage Point.

This discovery raised critical questions that needed urgent answers:

1) If the patient's disease or symptoms are cured independently of Assemblage Point correction, will their Assemblage Point move to a more beneficial location of its own accord?

2) If the Assemblage Point does move by its own accord, how long will it take?

3) How effective is Assemblage Point correction in assisting the patient's recovery from physical disease?

4) If the patient's Assemblage Point is corrected, will they recover from their physical disease?

5) If a patient's Assemblage Point was accidentally shifted due to some illness or trauma earlier in their life, was their current illness brought on by that accidental shift?

6) Would recapitulating the incident that caused the accidental Assemblage Point shift help the patient to recover?

In order to answer any of these questions adequately, it became essential to find a way of treating and curing the patient's physical symptoms independently of correcting their Assemblage Point.

This would provide an answer to the first question: if the patient's symptoms or disease are cured independently of Assemblage Point correction, will their Assemblage Point move to a more beneficial location of its own accord?

As it was evident from the patient's own accounts of their disillusionment concerning the medical treatments which they had undergone unsuccessfully, a completely new approach to medicine was necessary.

To solve these problems, effective medical treatments had to be designed. The author developed a number of electronic gem therapy instruments for treating diseases with which the patients were presenting. Fourteen years ago, a limited number of small battery-powered therapy instruments were designed and built. These instruments had an output power of only one tenth of a watt, but nevertheless proved most useful and effective for simple complaints. In practice, however, they were tedious to use and treatment times were too lengthy, typically requiring thirty minutes or more. Alongside the research and development of the Assemblage Point management therapies, the sophistication of the electronic gem therapy equipment rapidly improved with each new generation of design. The treatment procedures improved and many new medical discoveries were made.

Electronic Medicine

These days most European clinics are equipped with expensive electronic therapy instruments. Preventative medicine clinics and doctors in Europe now provide colour therapy, electronic gem lamp therapy, electro-laser acupuncture, transcutanious electro-neural simulator devices (T.E.N.S. therapy) and light therapy for their patients. Integrating frequencies, gems, colour and electronic amplification in one instrument produces a therapy which is many times more versatile and effective than other systems. Changing the colour and frequency of our biological energy affects the way our nervous system operates and our state of health.

Today, clinics, surgeries and doctors are able to use electronic gem therapy instruments thousands of times more powerful than those used previously. These can be used to target several different parts of the body at the same time. The special low-voltage lamps contain lenses which focus the gem rays so that the patient's problem can be specifically targeted. The gem stones and coloured filters are contained in a special chamber deep inside the lamp body. The gem lamps are connected to a precision electronic instrument. The instrument's digital monitors display the treatment intensity and vibrational rate. The patient's treatment can be selected by simply pushing the appropriate switch. Combining natural healing frequencies with colour and gem stones can influence the cohesion and vibrational rates of cells, organs and glands (see Figures 7.13 and 7.14 on page 160). The level of the biological energy or life force in them can be increased, and its quality adjusted and controlled by the doctor or nurse.

WARNING

Readers must not confuse "Electronic Gem Lamp Therapy" with colour therapy, light therapy or crystal therapy — all of which are different and will produce very different results. Coloured light bulbs, for instance, will exacerbate most skin conditions, also the heat emitted by them will dry the skin. Coloured light bulbs cannot be used to treat internal organs. There is a danger of injury, burns and electrocution from mains voltage colour bulbs as they can spontaneously implode (See Appendix IV, V & VI).

A voluntary worker in the Manchester area of the United Kingdom acquired electronic gem therapy equipment for her own use and to treat her family. The success of the lamps at fixing her family's health problems spread and very soon she was asked to visit elderly patients in their homes and give them treatment. Her patients also included a local priest and the staff and children of a nearby Catholic orphanage. After two months, she had experienced so much success that she was asked to treat patients at a nearby hospital. She and her partner were interviewed by consultants and asked to give a demonstration to the nursing staff. Later she accompanied the district nurse to patients' homes and administered treatments for complaints such as varicose ulcers and immobility problems. This story illustrates the simplicity, effectiveness, and reliability of electronic gem therapy.

To Cure — Target The Source of The Patient's Disease

The low-voltage, low-heat lamps are completely safe to use. The gems themselves never wear out or depreciate in value. Once acquired, there are no further expenses. Nothing is ingested, so there are no side-effects. The techniques and equipment design has been refined to include automatic treatment selection, so that specialised training or knowledge is not required and treatments can be safely delegated to junior staff. The focussed energy output can be felt on the skin as well as at deep tissue and organ levels. Patients find the coloured light and gentle energy given off by the gem lamps relaxing and pleasurable. Unlike drug therapies, the doctor or nurse can observe results as therapy proceeds. Ninety percent of patients can feel the energy almost instantaneously and give feedback to the practitioner. The patient can judge immediately if the therapy is effective and correct, because symptoms will reduce rapidly. The "get worse before getting better" reaction does not apply in the case of gem lamp therapy.

The lamps modulate or influence the atomic vibrational rate of the cells being treated. Therefore, if the wrong treatment is administered, it can easily be corrected by changing the type of gems, coloured filter and frequency. Any incorrectly given treatment can simply be erased and reversed. For example, an incompatible treatment would be ruby applied to a patient's sprained ankle. The hot rays of ruby would aggravate the pain and swelling and the patient would very quickly complain of an increase in pain. Changing to cool emerald and blue sapphire would immediately erase and replace the modulation that the ruby treatment induced. All types of pain and trauma must, in the first instance, be addressed with an analgesic calming treatment. This is done to remove the trauma from the gyroscopic electronic memory of the cell's atoms. The procedure can be likened to an audio or video cassette tape recorder. Before a new song or scene can be recorded on the magnetic tape cassette, the recording machine must first erase any previous recordings made on the cassette tape. If the tape recording machine did not erase them, then the new recordings would be distorted with the old recordings.

Contact with the patient's body or removal of clothes or dressings is often unnecessary, but it can be helpful. Gem energy can pass through clothing and dressings, but the colour-filtered light cannot. Applying the gem lamps close to the unclothed skin will permit shorter treatment times and greater accuracy at targeting internal organs or glands. Gem therapy lamps improve the patient's complexion, energy levels and mood, these changes should be apparent after 20 minutes of treatment.

Although electronic gem therapy lamps are completely effective on their own, they can, however, be valuably employed in conjunction with surgery, allopathy, psychiatry, physiotherapy, osteopathy, chiropractic and the various complementary support therapies. The following examples demonstrate the simplicity and effectiveness of treatment procedures for various conditions. When reading these, it will be found helpful in understanding the process of each treatment to refer to Figures 7.13 and 7.14 on page 160.

Acute and Chronic Pain

When we are asleep or in a trance, we do not experience pain. The frequency of the brain waves is Delta for sleep and Theta for trance. Every part of our body is connected to the brain via the nerves. Nerves carry the electrical signals back and forth between the brain and the body. As we fall asleep, the body experiences slow Delta brain waves in the nervous system. Our organs relax, the heart rate slows, blood pressure drops, muscles relax, and our aches and pains disappear. Usually, when we awake, the pains of the previous day are gone, therefore we can conclude that the vibrational rates associated with sleep heal the body. The frequency of the sleeping brain is about 1.5 Hz or cycles per second. Common sense suggests that applying Delta brain wave frequencies to the site of an injury will reduce pain. In fact, these frequencies are used in electronic acupuncture and T.E.N.S. therapy for exactly that purpose; however, the efficiency of those therapies is not very good. The gem to use in every case of pain is blue sapphire. Sapphire emits a calming, analgesic biological energy and increases endorphin production. Unlike analgesic and tranquillizing drugs, which can cause stomach disorders and other

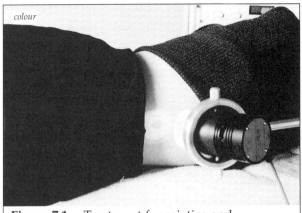

Figure 7.1   Treatment for sciatica and
prolapsed disc.

side effects, sapphire does not deplete the patient's energy reserves or
cause side-effects. On the contrary, the violet biological energy emitted by
sapphire fills the person with an uplifting tranquil energy. Sapphire rays
are many times more effective than analgesic or distalgesic drugs.

In the case of sciatica, violet-filtered light and blue sapphires are pulsed
once or twice a second (Figure 7.1). The site of the spinal injury can be
located, if necessary, by moving the gem transducer lamp up and down
the patient's spine. The patient will experience a decrease in pain as the
gem lamp is passed over the injury. It is also helpful to treat the back and
sides of the knee joint of the affected leg with a second lamp. This
treatment will completely relax all associated muscles and take the
pressure off the inflamed nerve, as well as reducing the nerve's
inflammation. The patient will experience profound relief. A single
treatment is often sufficient to clear up the condition, as illustrated below.

Case 27. Sciatica

*Mr A.G., Cumbria. November 1996. A local shopkeeper telephoned one evening
in urgent need of help. He was suffering from sciatica and the pain was severe. As
he was self-employed, he felt unable to take time off from his business. He arrived
at the door in obvious discomfort and hardly able to walk. Thirty minutes later,
after treatment with blue sapphire and violet light pulsed at Delta, he was pacing
the surgery to test the treatment. He was amazed at the level of pain relief and was
able to continue working. In the long-term, he was also advised to consult a*

specialist because his pelvis was misaligned, causing his spine to twist and putting pressure on his spinal nerve. His case was followed up over a period of 1 year and he had no recurrence of the pain.

Case 28. Back Pain

Mrs S.B., Lancashire. 1997. A 58 year old lady had received physiotherapy and ultrasound without success. She was unable to lift her leg up and was in some considerable pain. Electronic gem therapy was given to her spine using carnelian, diamond and sapphire. After 20 minutes, she could lift her leg and was a very happy lady. A week later, I met this lady and asked how she felt. She told me "The day after the treatment I felt so good I spring cleaned upstairs and threw a lot of things away, placed them in a plastic bag, then threw it down the stairs and went with it". I replied, "I did tell you to take it easy even if you feel great!".

The same treatment was also effective for a cancer patient presenting with chronic pain from nerve damage as a result of surgery for the removal of tumours. She found that sapphire treatment was more effective than her morphine tablets.

Pain associated with new injuries such as surgery, burns, cuts, abrasions, fractures, sprains or bruises should be treated with a mixture of blue sapphire and emerald with green filtered light. The cool rays of emerald rapidly introduce cold biological energy into the hot, injured cells. The redness will subside, and the swelling will be reduced. Bruises and blood clots can be rapidly dispelled with a diamond and carnelian mixture and an orange filter.

Emotional Shock And Exhaustion

The pain and emotional shock experienced through bereavement, for example, or a serious accident is very disruptive to the nervous and endocrine systems. It can ruin the appetite and sleep. If the situation persists for any length of time, the patient will become exhausted. When this occurs, infections can take hold, causing further biological energy depletion. This situation can be extremely dangerous as the patient's Assemblage Point may shift down to a problematic location.

We know from the scientific studies of sleep that the body heals itself during sleeping (Delta brain frequencies) and that the emotions can be healed through dreams (Theta brain frequencies). Directing blue sapphire rays and violet-filtered light at each side of a patient's head induces calming biological energy directly into the brain's hemispheres. The experience is very pleasurable as the energy travels down, via the nerves and blood supply, to every part of the body. Enhancing the gem and colour treatment with the Theta (dreaming) frequencies will induce a profound state of relaxation. This is accompanied by waves of pleasure which permeate the whole body. These "pleasure" waves smooth out emotional disturbances. This therapeutic procedure is named "bliss therapy" (see figure 5.9 in Chapter Five). Sometimes a small quantity of diamond is added to the sapphire to bring greater clarity and colour to the experience. With eyes closed, many patients report seeing colours. As treatment progresses, the colours become more vivid and are sometimes accompanied by visions or images. The therapy is extremely beneficial and improves the Assemblage Point location; the success rate is over eighty percent.

Currently, approximately seventy percent of all patients attending for gem therapy will receive twenty minutes of profound relaxation therapy before they are given the specific treatment for their complaints. Working with a fully relaxed patient saves the clinician or therapist time and energy, and allows the patient to be more receptive to any other treatment which they require.

Case 29. Depression and Pain

Mrs. R., Uxbridge. 1999. This sixty year old housewife and mother complained of painful left and right knees, involuntary shaking of the legs and depression.

Treatment 1. Lamps 1 and 2 were fitted with sapphires, violet filter, 3.3 Hz, Delta. The lamps were positioned on either side of the head for 20 minutes duration to completely relax her. The same lamps (i.e. using sapphires with violet filter) were then positioned on each side of the right knee for 20 minutes and the left knee for 20 minutes, using 1.5 Hz, Theta.

Treatment 2. As a result of Visit 1 there was an immense reduction of pain in the right knee and some reduction of pain in the left knee. The depression had ceased. The treatment carried out on Visit 1 was repeated, with the exception of the treatment to the left knee, which was changed to lamps 1 and 2 having carnelians and diamonds with yellow filter, positioned on each side of the left knee for 20 minutes, at 8.3 Hz, Theta.

Treatment 3. Patient reported that there had been no pain in the right knee but slightly more pain in the left knee. The left knee was then treated with lamps 1 and 2, applied to both sides of the knee simultaneously, having sapphires and emeralds with a green filter for 20 minutes, 1.5 Hz, Theta.

Treatment 4. Patient reported a great reduction of pain in the left knee. The same treatment given in Visit 3 was repeated.

Treatment 5. Patient reported left knee 95% better. Treatment was given as in Visit 1.

Treatment 6. Patient reported only occasional twinges in the left knee and no pain remaining in the right knee. Treatment as given in Visit 1 was repeated but not applied to the right knee. This patient had also had involuntary trembling in the knees and legs but this had been almost totally cured by the treatment. The only slight trembling remaining was apparently felt by the patient inside the body but was no longer detectable to anyone else.

Nervous Disorders

The Indian and Tibetan pharmacopoeia recommends sapphire for conditions like anxiety, panic, psoriasis, alopecia, migraine, and insomnia. Research has already shown that many nervous disorders are accompanied by High Beta brain frequencies.

Most nervous disorders and diseases respond positively to blue sapphire. Slow, calming frequencies should be used with violet-filtered light. A fast heart rate and high blood pressure can be slowed down with this type of treatment. Emerald is also important in the treatment of some nervous conditions. Emerald stops diarrhoea and, in a healthy person, may cause temporary constipation. A mixture of sapphire and emerald is used to treat irritable bowel syndrome. The bliss therapy, mentioned above, can be also employed and, in addition, the patient's abdomen is treated with a third gem lamp containing an emerald and sapphire mixture. The slow frequencies of Delta are employed to induce slower and smoother peristalsis and to cool intestinal inflammation. At the same time, the practitioner may calm the liver and gallbladder with emerald and sapphire lamps, should they be agitated.

Case 30. Irritable Bowel Syndrome, Cystitis and Arthritis

Mrs D.L., Lancashire. 1997. A 59 year old lady had had irritable bowel syndrome, cystitis and arthritis for quite a number of years. She was given electronic gem therapy to the area around the abdomen with emerald and sapphire lamps. The pain left after 15 minutes. The same treatment to the hips, knees and neck produced pain relief; the bladder was treated with emerald. After a few weeks her I.B.S. and cystitis had cleared up and the patient was able to stop taking the antibiotics which her doctor had said she would have to take for the rest of her life.

Skin Diseases

Psoriasis, Scleroderma, eczema, dermatitis, acne, warts, varicose ulcers, bedsores and pressure wounds are some of the many hundreds of skin diseases which can be healed or very significantly improved with electronic gem therapy lamps. Many skin problems are analogous with diseases of other organs; therefore, often, treatment does not involve treating the skin directly but the deficient or malfunctioning organ which is responsible for the patient's condition may be treated. Psoriasis is one of the more common complaints, with several millions of patients suffering from it in the United Kingdom alone. The costs to national health services and tax payers for preserving psoriasis with ineffective emoluments and hospitalisation runs into several billions of pounds each year. The same is true for eczema. The medical view published on one current psoriasis information leaflet states, "At the moment a permanent cure has not been found". As psoriasis is exacerbated by stress and worry, this kind of negative propaganda is more or less guaranteed to shift the patientis psychological temperament into appeasement or even apathy which further feed their symptoms. It also increases the profits of psoriasis supportive medications, research programmes and charities. The psoriasis patient receiving orthodox treatment is indeed an unfortunate one. Electronic gem lamp therapy can give very considerable benefits to those suffering from psoriasis. Many patients treated have not had their psoriasis return, even after several years after treatment.

Psoriasis responds well to treatment with sapphire, violet-filtered light and slow relaxing Delta frequencies. One patient developed psoriasis two weeks after she learned that her husband, a long-distance lorry driver, had cataracts and was likely to lose his job. She presented for treatment with both her hands red and raw, and so painful that she had to wear protective cotton gloves constantly. Conventional medical treatment had done nothing to alleviate her condition. A single twenty minute treatment began to reverse her condition and new healthy skin was visible after three days. A sixteen year old girl developed psoriasis after her parents divorce. She had been prescribed several different steroid creams, but the condition continued to spread. She was frightened and upset, and had been told that she might suffer with psoriasis intermittently for the rest of her life. With a single treatment of sapphire to her head, she made a dramatic recovery, two years later she had not experienced any re-occurrence.

Psoriasis is a disease in which skin cells behave erratically, by multiplying and dying too quickly. The skin drops off in flakes leaving sore, red patches. The affected skin can be treated directly with lamps. However, using sapphire to calm the top of the patient's head is much more effective. This treatment stops itching in a few minutes. There is a type of psoriasis which will not respond to sapphire but responds to the same treatment which banishes warts. Warts and psoriasis are considered by some doctors to be a type of cancer. Indeed, long term psoriasis patients are sometimes prescribed chemotherapy. Subjecting the patient's whole body to the debilitating effect of chemotherapy drugs in order to reduce the cellular biological energy of the skin is medicine in desperation.

Case 31. Psoriasis

Ms L.G.N., England. 1997. This 26 year old lady was feeling conscious of her psoriasis as she had booked a holiday with her boyfriend. On examination, she was also found to be suffering from irritable bowel syndrome (I.B.S.), but was not bothered about this as she was on medication from the doctor. Blue sapphire lamps were used on her crown to calm her down. Also, emerald and sapphire were used on the left side of her abdomen and above the navel. After 5 days, the I.B.S. had gone; the psoriasis was still there, but had calmed down and was waning.

Case 32. Psoriasis

Mrs. J.F., Lancashire. 1997. A 57 year old lady had suffered from psoriasis on her back, legs and elbows for 30 years. She was treated with sapphire to the crown of her head to reduce her excessive nervous electrical activity. The same treatment was used on psoriasis patches up and down the legs. The patient also complained

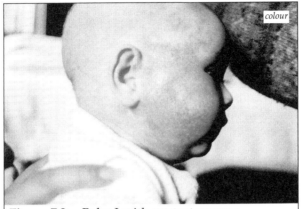

Figure 7.2 Baby J with contact eczema.

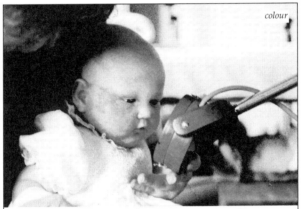

Figure 7.3 J's eye infection is given yellow sapphire rays.

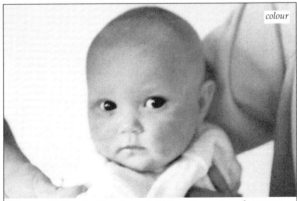

Figure 7.4 J after two full treatments of emerald and sapphire.

of pains in her hips and knees, for which her doctor has been prescribing drugs for the past 2 years. This was treated with sapphire and emerald lamps to her hips, knees and elbows. Both the psoriasis and pain diminished and cleared within 8 weeks.

Eczema and dermatitis are treated with emerald and green-filtered light. Treating the affected skin will reduce redness in minutes. Sapphire should be included if irritation is present. The number of babies suffering from eczema is on the increase. Five years ago, the figure was one in ten. Today, it is one in seven. Treatment with electronic gem lamp therapy may effectively reverse this trend. Certain types of eczema and acne require a stimulating treatment to improve local circulation. Other types require treatment to the liver and spleen.

Case 33. Contact Eczema

Baby "J", a 4 month old baby girl. March 1996. The following is an abstract from the medical case notes for "J", accompanied by three colour photographs illustrating her treatment using non-contact electronic gem therapy lamps.

At her first visit (26 March), "J" was suffering from contact eczema (figure 7.2). Her mother reported that the eczema had spread all over her body. It had originated near her right eye after she received chloramphenicol medication to the eye. She had a "sticky eye" condition. "J" and her mother had stayed in hospital while "J" underwent various unsuccessful therapies during which her mother reported that "J" became increasingly distressed. Her hands and arms were bound and restrained to stop her from scratching away her remaining skin. Other physical symptoms were swollen thyroid and glands, as well as elimination abnormalities which included green coloured faeces. Her general behaviour was extremely distressing and volatile.

She received a short, mild treatment of cool emerald and calming blue sapphire to establish her response.

At the second visit (11 April), there was a 15% general improvement in her condition. She received a full 20 minute treatment to her skin and liver area. During the treatment, "J" became increasingly exuberant.

At the third visit (22 April), there was a 50% improvement in her condition after the second treatment, with new healthy skin growth establishing more ground (figure 7.3). The eczema was contracting back towards the original point of contact, her right eye. This eye was treated using blue and yellow sapphires.

Her mother reported that she had had more energy than usual after her previous treatment.

At the fourth visit (7 May), there was a 90% improvement in "J"s condition, including her affected eye (figure 7.4). Her mother reported that it was an absolute joy to have her baby back to normal. She had been ill for so long that she had forgotten how much she had enjoyed "J" before

The blood disorders which can result from the use of chloramphenicol are very severe. According to Dr. L. Lanymore-Lim, in *Poisonous Prescriptions*, they can include aplastic anaemia, which may result in leukaemia, nausea, fever, vomiting, peripheral neuritis, erythema, diarrhoea, optic neuritis and Gray's Baby Syndrome. Dr. Lanymore-Lim states, "I am of the opinion that we should question the use of chloramphenicol in babies who suffer mild conjunctivitis or sticky eyes. Bathing with cotton wool balls moistened with warm water, although tedious, may be as beneficial and less harmful". It would seem that Baby "J"s chloramphenicol eye drops tracked down her tear ducts into the back of her mouth and aggravated her liver and bile, causing her eczema.

In the case of skin problems, the treatment given to the patient varies according to the type and the cause of the skin problem. Below are a few examples, which will indicate the depth of the research. With skin problems one can expect and obtain at least an 80% success rate with usually no more than three treatment sessions. In the case of youngsters with skin problems (and asthma), one can expect close to 100% success often with a single treatment.

EXAMPLE A

Where the patients skin cells are behaving erratically with continual flaking skin, the condition can be rapidly calmed down and eliminated by calming down the nervous electrical activity in the dermis and the brain. This is achieved by shining a dark violet lamp containing blue sapphires. The sapphires are electronically stimulated inside the lamp at the human frequency of sleep (1.5 cycles per second). Sapphire rays eliminate pain and have a profound calming and soothing effect on the patient which is an extremely pleasant experience. This calms down the biological energy of the patient and the skin cells. If the patient's skin is extensively affected, two lamps placed so that the light shines on each side of the patient's head induce profound relaxation. As the treatment proceeds, the patient's blood pressure and heart rate become calmer and the skin irritation subsides. In most cases, this therapy is sufficiently effective to cause the condition to clear up. If it is only the patient's skin which is affected in a particular area, then the lamps are generally used only to target the problem location.

EXAMPLE B

The above treatment will not be effective where the patient's skin has a wart like or lumpy appearance. This condition requires and responds rapidly to a stimulating lamp treatment using a yellow filter and citrine gem stones stimulated at a faster frequency of 8.5 cycles per second. This treatment is also effective for warts, a single 10 minute exposure will get rid of warts. (It is not understood why this treatment works; it is noted that ground citrine paste is applied to warts in Indian and Tibetan medicine).

EXAMPLE C

Neither of the above treatments will work in the case where the patient's liver is hot, sweaty and overactive and the skin condition looks both like psoriasis and eczema, perhaps with fluid discharging from the dermis. These types of symptom respond rapidly to a calm cooling lamp treatment targeting the patient's liver, using a green lamp containing a mixture of emerald and blue sapphire gems electronically stimulated inside the lamp at the human frequency of sleep (1.5 cycles per second). This treatment cools and calms down the overactive biological energy of the patient's liver in minutes. This can easily be confirmed by physically examining the liver with the hand, also the patient will report that they feel better as the treatment progresses, together with a remarkable improvement in their complexion. In addition, the patient's blood pressure and heart rate become calmer.

EXAMPLE D

Certain types of acne, eczema, dermatitis and urticaria, will respond to the above treatments and others will not and require a very stimulating treatment to improve the condition of the blood and circulation. Depending on the patient's overall symptoms and examination results, the following treatment may be given to the affected dermis and/or the liver, and/or the spleen. The spleen is responsible for the quality control of the blood and, in many diseases, we have found that targeting the patient's spleen with an invigorating treatment using an orange filtered lamp containing a mixture of white diamonds and orange carnelians, using a stimulating frequency, will clear up many skin and other common conditions. This therapy increases the vitality, biological energy and efficiency of the spleen and all of the blood which passes through it as the treatment proceeds. The energised blood passes or imparts its energised condition to all of the patient's organs, dermis and bones. For those patients who are rundown and low in biological energy, this therapy induces a profound feeling of well-being. This particular therapy is not only effective for skin problems, it is also effective for oedema (often accompanied with skin problems), varicose ulcers, asthma, sinus problems, senile dementia, strokes and many others diseases, including some diabetic conditions.

Viral And Bacterial Infections

In autumn and winter, biological energy falls as the Sun weakens and we become more susceptible to infection. There are more infectious organisms in the air due to the autumn decay everywhere. Humans also suffer a downward turn in biological energy, contract infections and pass them on. Sluggish, sickly, dying and dead cells are easy prey to invading micro organisms. Viral infections, such as the common cold and influenza, take hold by infiltrating the cell membranes in weak or stressed areas of the body, such as the throat, nose and lungs. Once inside a weak human cell, the virus multiplies and spreads to other cells throughout the body. Conserving, and thus maintaining, high personal levels of biological energy is the best way to avoid infections.

Orange carnelian lowers the temperature and diamond invigorates the system, dramatically increasing patients' energy levels. Influenza and colds respond quickly to a carnelian and diamond mixture with orange-filtered light at low Beta frequencies. The sinus, nose, throat and chest should be energised. If the infection is acute, treatment of the patient's spleen to energise it and the blood that passes through it on its way to the liver gives immediate relief. Carnelian and diamond can be used for the prevention of infections, since they increase cellular coherence and membrane resilience by increasing the levels of biological energy and the cells' vibrational rate. Asthma and bronchitis also respond well to this treatment. Where an infection involves bacteria, yellow sapphire or emerald are more effective. Yellow sapphire is frequently used to treat bacterial infection of injured tissue. Diamonds and carnelians are the preferred treatment for viral and yeast infections including candida, which responds well if the spleen is energised..

There is now substantial evidence to suggest that the rays of emerald (and yellow sapphire) reduce the ability of bacteria to multiply. Emerald reduces sexual libido in humans, so there is good reason to suspect that it will do the same to bacteria. Once bacteria have lost the ability to subdivide and multiply then it is a simple matter for the body's immune defence system to kill those which are remaining.

Returning from an extensive white water rafting expedition in the Himalayas, a friend called into the office on his way to his G.P.. He had contracted virulent dysentery while in India.He had suffered acute diarrhoea and vomiting for weeks on end and had lost 13 kilograms in weight. He was now experiencing a recurrence of his symptoms. He was instructed to go on to his doctor's appointment and return for treatment afterwards. On his return, he said that his family doctor could only advise not to eat and arrange for samples to be sent to the hospital for analysis. On examination his liver was very hot and was obviously infected. His liver was treated with emerald rays for 20 minutes. He telephoned the next day to say that his symptoms had gone, that he was feeling normal and that the area around his liver was now very cold. His case was followed up six months later and he was clear of the infection. This case is typical of the deadly efficiency of emerald in dealing with acute bacterial infections and cooling down damaged or infected tissue and organs.

On another occasion, late one Friday afternoon, a foreign gentleman came hobbling into a clinic, supported by a concerned friend. The man had an infected foot, the infection of which was so advanced that the smell from the wound was unbearable and could be detected in the clinic's reception area. His antibiotic medication had done nothing to alleviate the infection. The therapist treating him was an experienced nurse and from her knowledge she thought that he would require months of attentive nursing before the infected wound would heal. She treated the injury with emeralds and sapphires, changed the dressing and told him to return on Monday. The

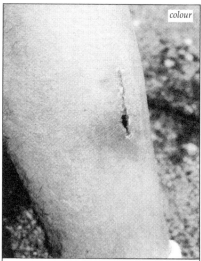

Figure 7.5 Infected leg injury with dermatitis complications.

patient returned on the Monday, delighted. To the amazement of the nurse, the infection had completely cleared and required no further treatment. The following example provides photographic evidence of treatment to infected wounds. The case illustrates the effectiveness of electronic gem therapy where standard drug therapies are ruled out due to conflicting symptoms and treatments.

Case 34. Infected Injury and Chemical Dermatitis

Robert, October 1996. Robert returned from a holiday in the Canary Islands with an infected leg injury. The injury had occurred 10 days previously. The infection was gaining ground each day (figure 7.5). The central part of the injury was becoming ulcerated. Robert also had skin burns and contact dermatitis covering 80% of his body. The dermatitis was caused by a faulty domestic water supply in the holiday accommodation. The water had contained dangerously high levels of chlorine. His travelling companion had also received similar skin burns from the water. Robert's doctor could not prescribe antibiotics for the leg injury because of the risk of exacerbating his dermatitis. However, he expressed his concern that, without antibiotics, the infection would spread. This view was confirmed by a second doctor.

Robert refused to use steroid creams. His view was that the applications of creams might dissolve the toxic chloramines (resulting from chlorine's reaction with the skin) deeper into the dermis, making matters worse. The burning, itching and stinging sensations associated with dermatitis indicated that a cooling treatment was required.

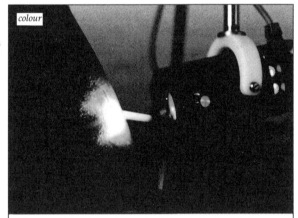

Figure 7.6   Treatment of the infected injury with yellow sapphire rays.

Robert's dermatitis was treated using a mixture of emerald and blue sapphire in a violet-filtered lamp. The rays were directed to the top of the head. The gem mixture was pulsed at a hypnotic frequency of 3.3 Hz (Theta brain wave frequency). Within a few minutes the irritation and itching subsided and Robert

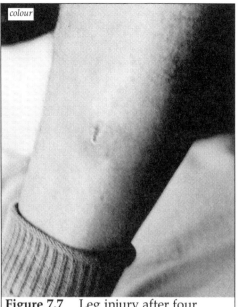

Figure 7.7   Leg injury after four short treatments.

was in a profound state of relaxation.

Simultaneously, his infected leg was treated with yellow sapphire with a blue lamp at 8.3 Hz for 15 minutes (figure 7.6). This treatment triggered the wound to discharge pus. Subsequently, the redness, swelling and pain subsided.

After seven days, his dermatitis had almost cleared, although the skin was burnt and patchy. His leg injury infection had improved and the top part of the wound had closed over. However, there was concern for the lower, ulcerated part. The wound was treated in a similar way to that of the first visit, described above. A second lamp containing stimulating diamonds with an indigo filter was first directed at the skin surrounding the injury and then directed through the bone from the back of the leg. This was to encourage the wound to heal from deep inside, rather than have the skin heal over a remaining infection. As the diamond treatment progressed, Robert experienced tingling energy sensations in his leg. The result of this drug-free, energy medicine treatment is shown in figure 7.7. Energy medicine was introduced into the cells of the infected tissue. It encouraged a healthy, uniform cellular vibrational rate with a higher biological energy and resulted in a rapid healing process.

Asthma and Allergies

The above cases and their successful treatment demonstrate that increasing or adjusting the patient's biological energy can eliminate viral and bacterial infections. It can also prevent infections in the first place. The domestic, farming, commercial and industrial pollution of the atmosphere, water and food has reduced the nation's level of biological energy. The number of patients experiencing allergic reaction symptoms has now reached epidemic proportions. This situation has created a growing business for the allergy hunter. Many newspapers and magazines now contain advertisements for practitioners who specialise in

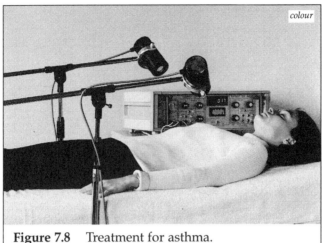

Figure 7.8   Treatment for asthma.

allergy testing. Complementing this is a large number of specialised businesses which provide numerous products claiming to give relief for hundreds of allergic conditions resulting from substances or environmental situations. These include air and water filters, cleaning materials and equipment, bedding and furniture, drugs, dietary supplements, remedies and therapies.

These are not real solutions. They do not address the problem. The problem is pollution and the low biological energy caused by the pollution of the environment. Increasing the biological energy of patients who experience allergies such as asthma, hay fever, food allergies and so on decreases their sensitivity. This approach can provide a real solution for the patient, but not our environment. Patients who experience allergic symptoms often suffer from a number of allergies. In the following case, the young lad had eczema and dermatitis.

Case 35. Asthma and Eczema

Harry, 5 years old. Uxbridge 1999. Harry was suffering from asthma and eczema at back of his knees, he also had a cold.

Treatment 1. Lamps 1 and 2 were placed each side of the head, using sapphires and violet filter, 3.3 Hz, Theta, 4.50 volts, for 10 minutes. For the eczema, lamps 1 and 2 were placed at the back of the knees, using emeralds and diamonds and a green filter for 10 minutes, 1.5 Hz, Delta, 4.5 volts. For the asthma, lamps 1 and 2 were used on the lungs at the front of the chest, using carnelians and diamonds with an orange filter, 8.3 Hz, Alpha, 4.50 volts, for 10 minutes. This was then repeated on the back of the chest for 10 minutes. Lamp 1 was then used with carnelians and diamonds and an orange filter, 8.3 Hz, Alpha, applied to the spleen for 10 minutes, 4.50 volts. Lamp 2 was used with topaz, 2 diamonds and carnelians with a blue filter applied to the nasal area, 8.3 Hz, 4.50 volts, Alpha, for 10 minutes. After treatment Harry looked and sounded 75% better. The next day his parents reported an almost complete recovery from all his symptoms and that he was exercising vigorously without breathlessness. His cold had completely disappeared. The parents were amazed that Harry's eczema had faded in a manner they described as "miraculous".

Treatment 2. Harry's asthma had returned a little and the eczema had receded. Lamps 1 and 2 were placed each side of the head, using sapphires with a violet filter, Theta, 3.3 Hz, 4.50 volts, for 10 minutes. For his asthma, lamps 1 and 2 were applied to the front of the chest cavity for 10 minutes, using carnelian and diamonds with an orange filter, 8.3 Hz, Alpha, 4.50 volts. The identical lamps 1 and 2 were then applied to the lungs on the back of the chest for 10 minutes. For the eczema, lamps 1 and 2 were applied to the back of the knees with emeralds and diamonds with a green filter, Delta, 1.5 Hz, 4.50 volts, for 10 minutes. After this treatment, Harry was almost totally free from asthma and his eczema had very largely disappeared and there followed a complete recovery.

The above case is one of several dozens of cases of youngsters suffering from asthma who have had their symptoms eliminated with a few treatments with electronic gem therapy lamps. After this type of energy medicine treatment, the patients have not had to return to using their inhalers or other respiratory medications. The treatment for asthma is to target the patient's lungs. However, simply energising the patient's spleen also produces good results by energising and purifying the patient's blood. When a patient is suffering from a number of allergies, targeting the spleen is a quick way to address them all at the same time.

Accidents And Injuries

New injuries such as cuts, burns, bruises, fractures and sprains require a cool analgesic energy, in which case emerald and sapphire are used with green light. When pain is present, inducing the sleeping frequency of Delta to the injured area can substantially reduce the pain and accelerate healing. Old injuries which are cold or numb require a stimulating energy and frequency to invigorate cells. A ruby and diamond mixture with red-filtered light, pulsed at High Beta frequencies, is used to invigorate the

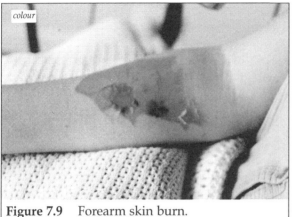

Figure 7.9   Forearm skin burn.

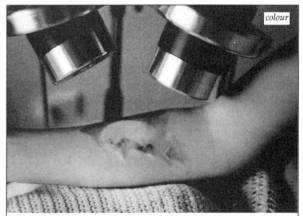

Figure 7.10   Treatment with two lamps
containing emerald and sapphire.

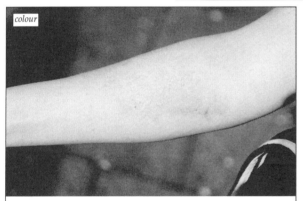

Figure 7.11   Accelerated healing process
over 5 days.

area with hot energy and improve the circulation. Infected injuries should be treated with yellow sapphire with blue-filtered light. To prevent infection spreading, the adjacent tissue should be invigorated with diamond and carnelian. The procedures can probably be modified to treat skin cancers.

Case 36. Skin Burn

Miss Kate T., aged 26. September 1997. Figure 7.9 illustrates a skin burn caused by spillage when removing boiling baked beans from a microwave oven. The injury was treated for 30 minutes with two lamps containing a mixture of emerald and sapphire using a green filter (figure 7.10). The patient reported that the burn had dried up completely by the following morning. The accelerated healing process can be seen in figure 7.11, which was taken 5 days later.

Prompt treatment of scalds and burns with emerald rays can prevent blisters forming. Never expose burns or new injuries to the rays of ruby. Ruby is for cold diseases.

Case 37. Chilblains

Miss C.G., aged 49, Lancashire. 1997. This lady had had chilblains since childhood and had never experienced any relief from medicine prescribed by her doctors. She was given electronic gem therapy for 20 minutes to relax her. Afterwards, ruby and diamond were used on her hands, feet and legs, with a red filter. This treatment cleared up the chilblains. Eighteen months later, the same lady was treated for an ear, nose and throat infection using carnelian, diamond and yellow sapphire/citrine with an orange filter.

Muscular and Skeletal Problems

Disabled patients suffering with spastic, athetoid, dystonic and choreiform muscular problems can be helped with sapphire and violet-filtered light. By pulsing the gem lamps at relaxing Delta brain frequencies, the brain signals which cause these conditions can be intercepted. The gem lamps are applied at appropriate nerve junctions on the spine or limbs. This treatment can relax tense muscles within minutes.

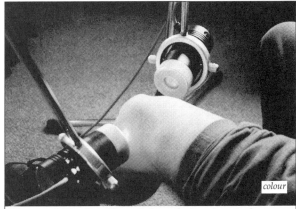

Figure 7.12 Cartilage injury being treated
with diamond and carnelian.

By utilising these techniques physiotherapists can treat more patients and be more effective. Rheumatism and arthritis respond positively to blue sapphire, which is very effective in dispelling the pain and muscular tension associated with these conditions.

Painful "clicking" cartilage problems in joints respond to diamond and carnelian lamps as they increase local circulation and biological energy. One patient had developed this problem as a result of a sports injury to his knee. After 10 minutes of this treatment, he said that his "bad" knee felt better than his "good" knee. The pain and swelling which accompany sprains, joint injuries and bone fractures should be treated with emerald and sapphire mixtures (Figure 7.12).

Case 38. Osteoarthritis with Muscular Sprain

Mrs. H., an 85 year old lady. Mrs. H. attended the clinic complaining of constant left hip and groin pain which had continued unabated for 6 weeks. She also complained of asthma which caused her to become short of breath at times. Mrs. H. could only walk using a stick and was limited to only a few yards of walking without pain. She had previously received physiotherapy exercises, ultrasound and chiropractic treatment to her hip without success. There were signs of moderate osteoarthritis of the left hip and inflammation of the soft tissues around the hip. Mrs. H. received five treatments of electronic gem therapy to her left hip. Five weeks later, she was free of pain and walking without the aid of her stick.

Case 39. Fractured Left Ankle

Mr. B., Hampshire. 1997. Mr. B., a 24 year old rugby player, had been unable to play rugby since fracturing his left ankle. Mr. B. complained of a sharp, deep-seated pain in his ankle when attempting to run fast or change direction at speed. Ultrasound and conventional physiotherapy had been unsuccessful at reducing his pain. Often fractures of the ankle cause significant soft tissue damage and scar tissue formation, and treatment aims to clear any deep-seated scar tissue that may be causing nerve irritation. In this type of injury, the frequency requirements seem to be dependent on the severity and duration of the injury (the longer the duration, the higher the frequency required), the extent of the soft tissue damage (the more damage, the higher the frequency), and the sensitivity of the patient. The more sensitive the patient (i.e. the more intuitive the patient and the more they can feel the treatment working), the lower the frequency required.

Treatment 1. Lamp 1 - just under the lateral malleolus of left ankle: blue sapphire, yellow sapphire, Mexican gold topaz; blue filter; 1200 Hz. Lamp 2 - inner ankle: carnelian; orange filter; 300 Hz. Response: significant reduction in pain during training, only slight twinges after two games of rugby.

Treatment 2. Repeat of first treatment. Response: continued improvement, no more discomfort.

Treatment 3. Changed treatment to try to clear final damage. Lamp 1 - outside of ankle: ruby; red filter; 25 Hz. Lamp 2 - inner ankle: gold topaz, diamond, carnelian; orange filter; 300 Hz. Response: ankle continues to improve with occasional twinges. Patient can now run at full speed without pain and he has returned to full-time rugby.

Case 40. Disc Prolapse and Sciatica

Mrs. B., Hampshire. 1998. Mrs. B. complained of severe low back pain, posterior thigh pain and leg and foot pain, which had continued unabated for 5 months. Mrs. B. attended a physiotherapy clinic and a disc prolapse was diagnosed. She had previously received intensive physiotherapy treatment which she had found to aggravate her condition. An examination confirmed the evidence of a L5- Sl lateral disc prolapse causing sciatica. A short course of chiropractic treatment was unsuccessful in reducing her pain. Electronic gem therapy was recommended. Mrs. B. reported that her pain significantly reduced after her first electronic gem therapy treatment. Her lower back and leg pain resolved after her second treatment. Mrs. B. had previously booked to go skiing with her husband prior to her injury. She decided to travel on holiday but was not going to ski. When she returned to the clinic, Mrs. B. reported that she had felt so well that she had been able to ski without any pain. Since her third and last treatment, Mrs. B. cancelled an appointment with her orthopaedic surgeon and remains pain free.

Case 41. Sprained Knee

Mrs. N., England, 1997. The patient was a 45 year old woman therapist who had torn a muscle in an amateur stage production. The noise of the muscle rupture was so loud it was heard in the second row. She was promptly incapacitated and in great pain. At her first visit a few days later, she was limping very badly, all other attempts at therapy having failed. She was initially given about 20 minutes of relaxing therapy with emerald and sapphire stones at Theta frequency (3.3 Hz). This very aware patient was able to report that her pelvis underwent a shift back into the normal energetic position during this stage. This was followed by about 30 minutes to the injured calf. All pain had vanished after this time, but a new pain had appeared in the opposite knee. This was probably due to the stress of limping and bearing all her weight on that side; this pain had necessarily been suppressed. A further 15 minutes on the uninjured side removed that discomfort as well, and she walked to her car without any discernible limp. The next day she phoned to say there was only mild discomfort, she was back at work, and she was happy with just one treatment.

The Future For Cancers And Degenerative Diseases

Recently a retired male patient was being treated for psoriasis with electronic gem therapy lamps. He was also diabetic and had lost the sight of his left eye. Several London eye specialists had told him that his loss of sight was due to blood clots (thrombosis) behind the eye affecting the blood supply to his optic nerve. His hospital specialists advised him that nothing could be done and that his sight would not return. He was treated with diamond and carnelian lamps to the side of his head around the eye. His eye sight returned whilst he was receiving treatment and has continued. In another case of blindness, a diabetic patient with kidney failure and dependent on dialysis, had his eyesight returned with a single treatment using the battery powered instrument shown in Appendix III, Figure A3.1. This same patient was also yellow with jaundice, his liver was stone cold when examined. He was treated with ruby gems to his liver and his colour returned to normal after treatment.

The same therapy procedures have been used to treat patients with senile dementia, or Alzheimer's disease, and stroke patients.. A retired male patient's mental and physical faculties had degenerated to the extent that he had become extremely problematic. His family had reluctantly decided that the only option was to place him in a nursing home. A single treatment with carnelian and diamond lamps to his head and spleen induced a remarkable recovery for him. His family reported that overnight his memory returned together with more physical energy. Prior to treatment he was more or less "a vegetable" but after electronic gem lamp therapy he was once again participating in family conversations, domestic activity and household chores, and also recovered his former sense of humour.

We have now seen, in the numerous cases given above, that, in order to bring about a satisfactory result for the patient, it has been necessary to target their internal organs or glands. These have included the liver, gallbladder, intestines, spleen, or brain; while some patients have also received treatment to other infected, injured or damaged areas of their body. This is a completely new approach to medicine and is long overdue. The following case gives a clear example of the effectiveness and the implications for future medicine which this new science present.

Case 42. Shock, Oedema and Possible Breast Cancer

Mrs. J.M., North of England. 1997. This patient, in her fifties, had been advised by her local hospital that she could have breast cancer. She was in a state of shock and depression and had reported to us for Assemblage Point assessment and correction. It was obvious in the initial interview that she was also suffering with oedema, or water retention, in the tissue of her arms, legs and feet, which she had had for a number of years. The patient was treated for oedema with electronic gem lamp therapy by stimulating her spleen with carnelian and diamond energy. Her Assemblage Point was corrected and she was given profound relaxation therapy with sapphire lamps. After several treatment sessions the patient's oedema was resolved and to her delight, after an examination, the hospital confirmed that the lumps in her breasts had cleared, as they could no longer be found.

Oedema is a blood condition and circulation problem. The spleen is responsible for cleaning and maintaining the quality of the blood. In a way, the spleen can be likened to a sewerage works which removes all of the offensive materials contained in sewage before returning clean water to a river. The quality of the blood stream is monitored and maintained by the spleen before it passes on its way to the liver. If the blood gets too dirty, i.e. should old dead red blood cells and other debris accumulate in the blood stream, then, just as with a polluted river, many very serious illnesses can result.

Like all muscles and other organs in the human body, the heart obtains its energy to pump the blood around the body from the blood itself. If the blood is dirty and weak in biological energy then all of the organs including the heart and the brain will be inefficient in their designated functions. As a result of impure blood, other organs and glands, such as the kidneys, will start to malfunction, compounding the problems. Treatment to the spleen rapidly improves the quality and biological energy of the blood. The improvement can be detected in the quality and firmness of the patient's pulse and in their complexion as the treatment proceeds. All of the patient's organs and glands receive a boost from this treatment and, for the very sick and the aged, it is especially effective. Energising the spleen and, therefore, all of their blood as it passes through the spleen, is very effective, not only for oedema but also other conditions such as varicose ulcers, acne, certain types of eczema, asthma, candida, thrombosis, strokes, senile dementia and probably many others.

Other degenerative diseases associated with the blood are leukaemia, Hodgkin's disease and A.I.D.S.. Cancer begins when a group of cells, or perhaps a single cell, start subdividing regardless of the body's need. These growths can form cysts and tumours and other very serious problems. The number of incidences of leukaemia are on the increase and it is considered to be a type of cancer. With leukaemia, the leukocytes or white blood cells do not mature. Healthy mature leukocytes do not multiply, but defend the body against invading organisms. The immature leukemic cells keep on multiplying and they are useless as an immune defence mechanism. The patient becomes extremely vulnerable to infections. The bone marrow produces red blood cells alongside white blood cells, so the patient also becomes anaemic and blood loses the ability to clot.

Psoriasis is the erratic behaviour of skin cells which multiply and die too quickly. Leukaemia is the erratic behaviour of white blood cells, but however in this case they do not die off. The cause of psoriasis and leukaemia is not known. Perhaps they are caused by some undetected toxin, dirt in the blood, virus or other agent which upsets the bone marrow, or they may be due to some spurious nervous system, electrical activity or endocrine system imbalance. Whatever the causes, current orthodox medicine has no effective treatment for psoriasis or leukaemia. Chemotherapy and radiation therapy are the normal methods used to kill off the excessive numbers of leukocytes. The dead leukocytes floating in the blood stream clog up and restrict the blood flow to various organs and glands of the patient causing malfunctions.

Psoriasis is treatable, as we have seen above, by calming the skin and the nervous system down using electronic gem therapy lamps. If erratic skin cells can be made to behave themselves, then it is conceivable to apply similar or modified procedures to the bone marrow and the blood to treat leukaemia sufferers. Perhaps the bone marrow is too cold and low in biological energy. Anaemia is a cold disease which responds to the hot energy rays of ruby. It is entirely possible that energising the bone marrow with ruby and diamond gem therapy lamps and energising the spleen as mentioned above might provide a turning point for leukaemia patients. It would also be possible to treat the immature reproducing leukocytes in the same way that bacterial infections were dealt with above.

Another rare degenerative disease which is also a form of cancer is Hodgkin's disease, in which there is erratic behaviour of the blood cells called lymphocytes and the associated lymphatic system. The lymphocytes play a major roll in the defence of the body against infections. The lymphocytes take a number of days to achieve sufficient numbers to cope with childhood infections, such as chickenpox. Children, being more vulnerable to infections, have proportionally a larger thymus gland than adults and, when an adult contracts an illness like chicken pox, it can be quite serious. With chicken pox and other bacterial infections there is a mechanism in the body which stimulates the body's ability to produce more lymphocytes to kill the invaders. In the case of Hodgkin's disease, there seems to be some type of continual message which triggers the body to continue to produce lymph cells. The thymus gland, spleen and bone marrow are responsible for the production of lymphocyte cells. Radiation therapy is often given to the thymus gland and elsewhere along with chemotherapy to prevent further production of lymphocytes. Whatever the cause which triggers the erratic cellular behaviour of the lymphocytes to produce Hodgkin's disease, it should be possible to address and reverse the patient's condition by perhaps calming the thymus gland, spleen and bone marrow with emerald and sapphire gem therapy lamps.

Acquired immune deficiency syndrome or A.I.D.S. is another degenerative blood condition. The T-lymphocytes produced by the thymus gland literally fall asleep. The lymphocytes do not function to protect the body against invading organisms. Opportunist infections take hold, even from organisms which normally do very little harm. With the body's lymphocytes out of action, it is only a question of time before the patient becomes sick.

Many persons who have been tested and found to be H.I.V. positive have not developed A.I.D.S. Within people who are H.I.V. positive but have not developed A.I.D.S., lymphocytes continue to function and protect them from invading organisms. It seems possible that the H.I.V. virus may not be the only agent which causes A.I.D.S., and that it could be a combination of H.I.V. with a low Assemblage Point location, low biological energy and endocrine imbalances which causes lazy lymphocyte functioning. Two common cancers which develop as a result of A.I.D.S. are Kaposi's sarcoma, a skin cancer and non-Hodgkin's lymphoma. Hodgkin's disease can be thought of as being the opposite to A.I.D.S., in so far as there is an unknown mechanism which triggers the body to continue to manufacture lymphocytes. With A.I.D.S., it is almost as if there is a second traitor mechanism present, perhaps in the blood stream, which reassures the lymphocyte colonies that everything is fine. Theoretically, it should be possible to increase the biological energy of the lazy lymphocytes. Stimulating the thymus gland and the spleen area with diamond and carnelian may help the production of resilient and active lymphocytes.

Other forms of cancers are on the increase and are said to be caused by the pollution of the Earth's atmosphere. The Sun's high frequency ultraviolet light, which formerly was absorbed by the Earth's upper atmosphere, and which, in the process created the protective ozone layer, now passes straight through to create skin cancers. The rays of ultra-violet light are deadly. They are used to disinfect water supplies from bacteria, yeasts and other living organisms. Ultra violet rays damage human skin at the molecular and atomic level. The result of this damage can cause malignant cancers which have to be surgically removed. Once again, theoretically, it is possible to calm and reduce the biological energy of cancerous tissue and increase the vigour of healthy tissue. Other action can also be taken to assist with cancer, such as energising the patient's blood and spleen as previously mentioned.

Generally the medical profession seems to believe that many patients suffering from some forms of genetic disease and genetic damage are incurable. Inherited diseases are said to be passed on by the genes or D.N.A. molecules at the time of conception. The D.N.A. molecules are very complex atomic structures which can easily be disrupted. Countless chemicals, such as benzine or the drug thalidomide, can adversely affect the D.N.A., causing cancer or other growth deformities. The same is true of radioactive materials, gamma rays, X-rays, ultra-violet light, microwaves and many other man made electrostatic and electromagnetic transmission fields. Gross energy can disrupt, modulate or change the structure of D.N.A. molecules, causing cancers, tumours and deformities.

Life has the ability to modify and improve itself in order to adapt to the ever changing environment on Earth. These changes are made to the D.N.A. molecule. The human body has the ability to change and modify D.N.A. molecules. Otherwise, how can we pass on improvements from one generation to the next? If we develop a resistance to a particular disease in our lifetime, later we can pass on this resistance to our children. For example, in the New World, chicken pox is often lethal for the natives, whereas Westerners can have an inherited resistance to its severity. There is a very subtle, invisible mechanism or power which initiates these infinitesimal molecular changes. Therefore, at any time, the D.N.A. can be changed by any living individual of any species of life on Earth. Science is unable to explain the subtle mechanism which causes the D.N.A. to change.

Patients suffering from a genetic disease should be given hope by electronic gem lamp therapy results. Several patients have been told by their doctor that they have developed a medical condition for which there is no cure. The patient's doctor or specialist concerned has based his opinion on the laboratory chemical testing of blood samples provided by the patient. Several such patients have attended for electronic gem lamp therapy and, as a result, have experienced a recovery from their symptoms. Subsequent laboratory blood tests for these patients have been negative. In other words, the chemical composition of the blood has changed as a result of electronic gem therapy. If gross energy can detrimentally change the chemical composition of a patient's blood, then it seems that there is a potential for the development of energy medicines which will heal D.N.A..

Case 43. Auto Immune Disease and Cirrhosis of the Liver

Age 54. The patient was incapacitated, due to a number of serious symptoms and was mainly confined to bed. The patient's symptoms included jaundice, hypertension, vertigo, nausea, breathlessness, hot sweating attacks and diabetes.

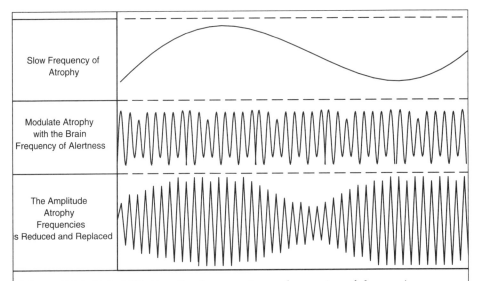

Figure 7.13 Rehabilitating the frequencies and energies of depression, atrophy, numbness, coldness or poor circulation

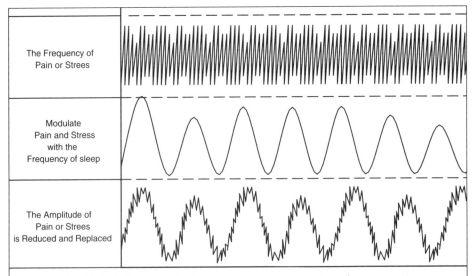

Figure 7.14 Rehabilitating the frequencies and energies of stress, pain, injures or infections.

The doctors and specialists had advised this patient's to enjoy life as much as possible. They did not have any solution for this degenerating condition.

On examination the patient's Assemblage Point was very low down, located just below the liver. The liver area was very hot and sticky when physically examined, whereas the spleen area was cold.

The patient's Assemblage Point was corrected and the liver cooled down with an emerald and sapphire lamp, using a green filter and slow calming frequencies (see Figure 7.14). At the same time the spleen was energised with a diamond and carnelian lamp, orange filter and faster Low Beta frequency (see Figure 7.13). As the treatment proceeded, the patient's jaundiced complexion improved by the minute. At the end of the treatment, the patient eliminated an abnormally high volume of urine.

This patient attended a total of six appointments. On each occasion, the patient's Assemblage Point had slipped down a little but less with each visit. The same gem lamp therapy was applied to the liver and the spleen on each visit, which raised the Assemblage Point back up to the centre. On each visit, the patient reported significant improvements in all symptoms and general condition, health and psychological mood. These improvements were visible to everyone who knew the patient prior to his treatment. Over a period of eight weeks, this patient returned to driving, country walking, professional duties, normal family activities and so on. Five months later, the patient's health has continued to improve.

Where life threatening disease is involved, this case demonstrates the effectiveness of adjusting and compensating for the malfunctioning of the liver and the spleen. This patient's cool, sluggish spleen was modulated with a faster stimulating frequency and warm invigorating gem lamp energy (see Figure 7.13) . At the same time, the patient's stressed hot liver was modulated with slow, calming frequencies and cool, analgesic gem lamp therapy (see Figure 7.13). This case also shows that psychological symptoms, i.e. the way we feel and experience reality, can be dominated by physical disease and that this is linked to the patient's Assemblage Point location. It also answers question number one at the beginning of this chapter, by demonstrating that targeting the source of the patient's disease will correct their Assemblage Point location. It should be remembered that the procedures used to treat psoriasis, eczema, varicose ulcers, sciatica, oedema, thrombosis, etc., illustrated in the case studies throughout this book, were, in the first instance, only theories. They proved to be successful when put to the test. From the perspective of hindsight they seem obvious. Before they were proved, most people hearing about them would have considered them unbelievable. Many patients, who were suffering from long-term diseases, who have been treated with electronic gem therapy lamps and experienced a rapid recovery, consider them to be "miraculous". Electronic gem therapy lamps are not a miracle, the procedures are based on sound, scientific principles. The background knowledge of gems which they utilise has been drawn from the experience of dedicated medical practitioners, spanning several thousand years.

Electronic engineering is precision science. Marrying this with the ancient knowledge of gem medicines has produced extraordinary surprises in only a few years. Electronic gem therapy lamps are still in their infancy. Their future development and the associated therapies will progress many times faster than new drug treatments. Drug development, partly due to the side effects drugs can cause, require expensive long periods of research and testing. In less than two decades of development, electronic gem therapy lamps are often producing far superior results to any equivalent drug therapies which are available for treatment of the same disease. This simple, safe, targeted energy medicine is giving reliable and repeatable results. Therefore, it is only a question of time before the public health services in different countries begin to employ it for their patients. In the United Kingdom, the success of electronic gem therapy lamps has reached sufficient numbers that there are now insufficient practitioners to meet the demand for treatment.

As time passes, more and more medical professionals are likely to employ Assemblage Point diagnosis and correction procedures, together with targeting electronic gem therapy lamps. Medical, educational and many other institutions will start putting money into further research. We can expect further exciting developments in preventative medicine and new effective treatment procedures for other disabling and life-threatening illnesses and diseases.

The Assemblage Point diagnostics and correction procedures have been a key factor and have assisted the rapid development of the numerous innovative medical procedures which employ the electronic gem therapy lamps outlined above.

Using Assemblage Point diagnosis, it has been possible to rapidly improve the patient's symptoms by keeping track of their energy levels. It is an indispensable aide to progressing seriously sick patients through therapy to a successful outcome.

Of all of the different possibilities with which life presents us, so far as our health, personal development and death are concerned, there is one thing which stands out above anything else as being of the most importance, and that is that we should all learn to crystallise our individual consciousness in our energy body. The easiest way to do this is to become aware of our own Assemblage Point location and that of our fellow beings and to understand the consequences associated with the numerous different locations.

Epilogue

Nothing that I have written is final, completed or closed. I feel that I should state my position, I am an independent medical scientific investigator and explorer. My loyalties are to objective exploration, objective experimentation and repeatable testable techniques and methods. I value above everything else calibrated scientific theories, techniques and methods which can be put to the test and verified by others. I abhor any kind of political or financial controls or manipulation, any kind of intimidation, covert hostility, dogmatic and fanatical behaviour and, on these and other ethical issues, I will not compromise myself.

All of the therapies that have been developed by myself have in the first instance been tested on my own body to verify that they are not harmful and that there are no side effects or unpleasant reactions. I would never subject a patient or any other person to any treatment which I have not personally experienced, even though I do not have the patient's disease or symptoms. Naturally at times I have been ill and have had several accidents, one or two very serious, these incidences have played a major part in the development of the Assemblage Point science and Electronic Gem Lamp Therapy. Perhaps in the future it may be possible to elaborate on my personal life, however one owes discretion to one's self and this is not the time or place to set this information down for all to read. I require more powerful allies before I will do this. Over the last 20 years, I have used my body as a test tube to establish the effects of many types of crystalline substrates. I have concluded from these tests and other tests that Electronic Gem Lamp Therapy is the safest and most effective and pleasant therapy available to date. As some crystalline substrates can have very powerful effects or produce unpleasant feelings for some people, this is not an endorsement for others to tread this path without expert knowledge.

The manuscripts, the basic contents of this work, were begun some five years ago. I have moved on during those five years. Inevitably one progresses, and many more discoveries have been made in this time, but not included in this work. Indeed, I have deliberately restricted the contents of this book to include only the bare minimum, the basic principles in their simplest form, for ease of understanding. I am well aware that a great deal of additional data and knowledge has been deliberately omitted or could not be included on this occasion.

Through 1995 and 96, I wrote three short articles about energy medicine and the Assemblage Point for a newly established medical journal, whose editors requested a fourth article expounding the details and applications of electronic gem lamp therapy. However, they refused to publish any details of the effects of drugs on Assemblage Point locations, saying that it would cause them problems with various medical authorities and government offices. In any event, the three articles were so popular that, in just a few weeks, they quadrupled the journal's subscriptions and recently the editors told me that 'neither before nor since has any other article attracted so much interest and attention'. The articles were placed on the Internet and the subsequent volume of mail, e-mails, visitors and patients which I received has been immense. The following letter from a practitioner is typical of many:

". . . your three articles carry an enormous weight. . . and are most interesting, and definitely the most novel and practical material on the net."

As the scientist who has exposed the Assemblage Point's existence and medical benefits, I am well aware of the future implications and consequences across a broad spectrum of human activity and endeavours. For many people its exposure in this book will bring about profound change for the better. I can say this as a person who has experienced these benefits at first hand and through others on thousands of occasions. In this respect, I am both very content and considerably relieved that this work is now going to press.

The enormous weight of the Assemblage Point knowledge is now shared with you, the reader. As I said, in the Introduction, this knowledge is power, the power to transform. I have indicated in detail how ignorance of the Assemblage Point is heavily implicated, if not totally responsible, for all kinds of disease and sinister situations. Human history is littered with examples of deliberate manipulation, albeit unconsciously, of the Assemblage Point for evil ambitions. Just like Albert Einstein's nuclear fission or Stephen Hawking's black hole, power does not take sides, it can be used for good or evil. Power has to be contained and tempered with sobriety and wisdom. The majority of people who have been exposed to this knowledge and these techniques have treated them with the respect and consideration which they deserve and have used and continue to use the methods to benefit their lives and those of others surrounding them.

Over the years, there have been several exceptions, as I have indicated throughout this book. There have been and will continue to be overtly and covertly hostile people who will attempt to corrupt, contradict or denounce the human Assemblage Point knowledge and deny ordinary people the freedom which it holds. There are many people and organisations with ambitions, charming facades or reputations, products, programmes or doctrinaires to protect. Others have financial and professional vested interests endangered.

People who are most at risk from the effect of these types of unethical individuals or organisations are those with low Assemblage Point locations, associated with disease, chronic grief, apathy or appeasement. Due to the chronic low state of psychological health or physical health, these people are easy prey to deception, the media and advertising propaganda. This is particularly true when large sums of money are at stake and the resulting public coercion through the media and advertising can be invisible and tenacious. It is a regrettable fact of life that individuals and organisations with Assemblage Point locations associated with chronic antagonism, anger or covert hostility, spend inordinate amounts of their time and money attempting to reduce enthusiastic and creative individuals or organisations down to locations of apathy, grief or appeasement and in some case disease and bankruptcy. I have included in Appendix I some letters of complaint from patients and others, together with actual case studies, concerning various types of therapy misrepresentations.

To counteract this type of negative and dangerous influence, it is necessary to publish the truth. In Berlin, I was standing with Dr. John Lilly by the famous wall. As we were standing there, reviewing the years of old graffiti painted on the wall, I said to John, 'The Berlin Wall is not only a monolith which represents the division between East and West, it also represents the division between the left and right brain, a division maintained by our dumb limited belief systems". I added, "When this wall comes down, the artificial barrier between man's left and right brain will disintegrate and humanity will evolve onto the next level". After quite some time he said, "You had better publish or go under". I replied, "Easier said than done". The following year the Berlin Wall was raised to the ground.

The contents of this book will open up a way forward, a new beginning, not just for mental, physical and social health, but also for many ordinary people. There will be an enormous amount of new research and other material generated by enthusiastic people from all walks of life, which will be of great interest to others. Other researchers and practitioners have personally experienced covert and overt hostility, especially from people with financial and professionally vested interests in medications, products or therapies which are overshadowed by the inconceivable successes of the Assemblage Point diagnostics and electronic gem lamp therapy. These types of unethical activities, in effect, not only compromise the patient's health and welfare for profit but, even worse, they prevent the advancement of medical science. It is not easy to get one's papers, experiences or views published. To partly solve this problem for everyone and to counteract negative influences, I have established a web site on the Internet for exactly this purpose and you can submit your papers, experiences and case studies to: theassemblagepoint.com or by normal post to the address given in Appendix IV.

"All it takes for evil to pervade is for good men to do nothing." Fortunately, our Assemblage Point is not a product, or a commodity, neither is it a philosophy, dogma, religion or a belief system. It is something far more tangible and scientific, it is something that we can become aware of, like a tool, get hold of and put to work, in the service of common humanity. From a pragmatic and scientific perspective, if we have our health, we possess time which is essential, since time provides the chance for all of us to find and experience what we want in life. To counteract the Assemblage Point locations of fear, intimidation, arrogance and ignorance requires knowledge. Today, the Assemblage Point knowledge is beyond doubt and the irony is that it has always been there, calmly standing by, waiting throughout eternity to be discovered. This knowledge is now available for everyone yet forcing itself on no man and it is free.

Postscript

There have been a number of misunderstandings concerning shifting the Assemblage Point. As I stated in the epilogue, I have not concluded this work. The details and theories relating to the Assemblage Point are a vast subject, with many different branches of research. My main objective in limiting the information to the bare essentials was so that this book did not become too complicated for readers and put them off adopting the techniques. However, due to a number of recent developments, I feel that it is necessary to clarify several critical points. There is one point that I feel duty bound to bring forward into this work concerning the shifting of the Assemblage Point. I regret that this text was compiled too late to insert into the bulk of the text.

There are three distinctly different classifications of types of movements or shifts that can occur with the Assemblage Point manipulation and these are:

> 1) A movement.
> 2) A shift.
> 3) A shift in depth

A movement of the Assemblage Point happens to most of us regularly. For example, if we are intimidated by violence or anger or even by legal processes, we can get very worked up and stressed. In these cases, the Assemblage Point will move to the right side and it can take several days or weeks for it to move back again. The person will gradually feel better by degrees as their systems re-balance. A movement is basically only a change in the Assemblage Point entry angle. The central core of the Assemblage Point energy has not shifted, although it will be located slightly differently on the front of the chest.

A shift is distinctly different from a movement. The Assemblage Point becomes dislodged and moves to a different location in the body. This can occur with a serious trauma of any kind. Generally, under these circumstances the Assemblage Point does not return to its original location naturally and the recipient becomes ill.

A shift in depth occurs only under very special or rare circumstances. A shift in depth occurs when the central core of the Assemblage Point energy moves closer to the surface of the chest or even outside the surface of the chest.This is a very powerful experience and it reinforces and stabilises the Assemblage Point location. The procedures for shifting the Assemblage Point by the techniques outlined in Chapter Five, under the sub heading "Clinical Shifting", produce a shift in depth. The depth of the shift depends on the skill and the available free energy of the person doing the shifting. These factors determine how far off the surface of the chest the central core of the Assemblage Point moves. This type of shifting increases the frequency and the energy potential of the Assemblage Point. The vortex becomes concentrated into a smaller diameter core and the point becomes much brighter in appearance and more visible.

Misrepresentations of the Assemblage Point

There are a number of alternative health practitioners who claim to shift the Assemblage Point by various means other than those outlined in this book. Most of these practitioners are talking about point "number one" above, i.e., moving the Assemblage Point, They are not shifting it.

If one can move the Assemblage Point to the right with anger or intimidation, then it is obvious that ecstatic experiences will move it to the left. Workshops where participants engage in dancing, singing, mediation, chanting, or yoga, in fact, any activity which is ecstatic, will move the Assemblage Point towards the left. Just as with a stressful experience, it will take some time for the participants to return to their normal entry angle or location and state of consciousness. The same thing happens when we fall in love. Our Assemblage Points moves and aligns towards that of our partner's. Sometimes, the high passionate energy of romantic encounters will create a shift in the Assemblage Point location.

I do not wish to spoil the enjoyment and benefits that these types of activities provide, and I would like to say that, from a health perspective, I am in favour of any type of physical or mental exercise. However, from the medical perspective, I have to say that the claims made by alternative therapists using these methods and claiming that they are shifting Assemblage Points is damaging for future developments. They will bring Assemblage Point shifting into disrepute.

Therapists who claim that they are shifting the Assemblage Point when actually all that is occurring with the therapy is a natural movement, cause confusion for patients who are seeking medical attention for their Assemblage Point. Singing, dancing, meditation or dancing will not cure M.E. or any other serious condition. Moving the Assemblage Point is not shifting it. A movement cannot compare to a shift in depth of the Assemblage Point.

Therapists who attempt to shift Assemblage Points of patients with serious health problems by methods other than those outlined in this book are downgrading the knowledge and wasting their patient's time. It also displays an ignorance of both medicine and the Assemblage Point and indicates that they have not received any professional training in the Assemblage Point or medicine and disease. Here is a letter which was published in a health magazine.

"I found the articles by Jon Whale very interesting. However, I do believe that one has to deal with the root of "whatever" altered the assemblage point in the first place, as well as correcting it. If the "software which caused the shift" has not been dealt with, sooner or later the assemblage point will move out of position again? It would be interesting to combine assemblage point moving with emotional stress release and detoxification etc".

This is a therapist, who, having read the articles and case studies, has identified with them only within her beliefs and particular field of interest. She did not understand them. What the letter suggests is that unless the patient receives psychotherapy, counselling, a course of detoxification supplements or colon irrigation therapy, etc. the patient will become ill again. She has not done any research work to establish what she says, it is just her belief.

If a person's Assemblage Point is sent crashing down to below the liver by some accident or trauma, why should the patient require detoxification or psychotherapy? It is regrettable that many recently introduced alternative therapies are based on limited human opinions or belief systems, advertising and propaganda, and there is very little sound scientific evidence to back them up.

Misrepresentations of Electronic Gem Lamp Therapy

There have been recently a number of deliberate misrepresentations of electronic gem lamp therapy both on the television, in the newspapers and in some magazines and other publications.

One commercial TV programme indicated another serious misrepresentation: that of implying that the lamps need to be part of a system of healing, that they will not be effective unless the patient also receives herbal preparations and dietary controls and manipulations.

This is medically nonsense; there are many hundreds of medical conditions that have absolutely nothing whatsoever to do with diet and would never respond to herbal preparations. Most Westerner's diets these days are, on the whole, very good and this type of propaganda is obviously credulous. Only a exploitable person is going to take this type of propaganda seriously. It is very damaging for alternative professionals who are doing good work.

This same television programme tried to impress viewers by throwing in a few scientific words here and there, to back up the unresearched and unsubstantiated cures that they were recommending to their viewers. In this programme, they referred to the electronic gem therapy lamps, which their guest practitioner was demonstrating on the programme, as "electromagnetic therapy" and also inferred that colour therapy was the same. The TV programme later issued a letter of apology.

Electromagnetic therapy has been around for the last century in numerous forms, represented by all kinds of different types of equipment. It is very cheap to manufacture, as it is only constructed from coils of copper wire and an electronic oscillator. It has not been adopted for medical use by orthodox medical practitioners. Medical doctors are not very well disposed to electromagnetic therapy due to the fact that it cannot be contained, it passes straight through brick walls and everyone around the patient receives exposure. But there is an even more sinister reason why medical doctors are very wary. Medical research has established that electromagnetic waves induce currents and voltages [EMF (electro motive force)] in human and animal tissue. It is scientifically proven that electromagnetic waves cause cancer, tumours and genetic damage as well as many nervous diseases. The skin wards in NHS hospitals have posters displaying to patients the dangers of electromagnetic radiation on their notice boards. In 1985, Dr R. Lin of the

Maryland Department of Health reported on an epidemiology study of people whose occupation would expose them to higher levels of electromagnetic radiation. His study proved that a significantly greater number of the exposed group developed brain tumours.

With regular articles appearing in the media highlighting the health dangers, electromagnetic pollution has become a major concern of many people and there are numerous products that take advantage of the fear created. There are several types of cheap battery powered gadgets that flash a red warning light when held within the vicinity of any type of electrical equipment.

I have heard several accounts concerning alternative therapists using these devices to intimidate their patients. These gadgets are not scientifically calibrated and their sensitivity can vary wildly from one product to another and some are so sensitive that they will flash a warning when held close to a wrist watch. Patients have been told that their watch is responsible for causing their health problem. Most of these gadgets serve little practical purpose, the measurement of electromagnetic radiation and its millions of different frequency components is very complicated and the equipment required is extremely costly. Only a person trained in electronic engineering will possess the knowledge and skills to operate these items properly and it is not a job for an alternative therapist who is unlikely to have the electronic qualifications necessary to give the patient a scientific evaluation.

Unlike electromagnetic radiation, the visible frequency spectrum, i.e. light, does not induce voltages into living tissue. Indeed, life cannot be sustained without light and Dr Richard Hobday's book, The Healing Sun, scientifically confirms this. This book includes a detailed and scientific account of the benefits of light for health, the dangers to health from lack of sunlight and an historical account of how, in the past, medical doctors have used sunlight to cure serious diseases.

None of the case studies contained in this book involved any therapy other than any medications which the patient's own medical doctor was prescribing, such as analgesics, antibiotics or insulin. The patients were not given or recommended to take any vitamins or mineral supplements, herbal or homeopathic medicines, psychotherapy, physiotherapy or counselling. No scientific studies have been carried out on the effects of combining electronic gem lamp therapy or Assemblage Point shifting with other modalities of medicine. Until such research is carried out and published, patients seeking treatment are well advised to take the precautions outlined in Appendix IV.

The gem therapy lamps apply much more than colour to the patient and no colour therapy is as effective as electronic gem lamp therapy or needs to be used in conjunction with it. Any therapist who insists upon the necessity of using additional medication, supplements or therapies when using electronic gem therapy lamps is possibly not acting in the best interests of the patient.

As the Assemblage Point knowledge spreads, there will be many people clambering onto the bandwagon. Those alternative therapists who are doing good work should document all of their cases and write them up and present their work in a scientific way for others to understand and make use of. I regret to have to say that this is the only way that the benefits of a particular therapeutic technique will gain credence in the medical world.

In this respect one has to bear in mind the average Assemblage Point location of Westerners. It is slightly on the right side of the chest and this indicates that the rational left side of the brain is dominant. It is a fact of life that the average person is a rational being. Therefore any material or theories which are not presented in a rational format will be disregarded out of hand as the average person will not understand them, or take them on board.

Appendix I

ASSEMBLAGE POINT TREATMENT AND RECORD FORM

For future reference and analysis it is essential to keep good written records. For this purpose two special forms are provided. If you are locating and shifting the Assemblage Point for personal growth and health improvements, where disease or physical symptoms are not a factor, then use the second form, the 'Assemblage Point Correction Record Form'. For your convenience, a number of these have been provided.

If the situation involves a patient suffering with a disease or symptoms, use the 'Medical Analysis and Treatment Record Form' and record as many details about the patient as is possible, including how they have been feeling towards life and what problems they have been experiencing. Get sufficient information to build up a good picture of the person or patient.

In all cases, follow the instructions in Figure A2.1, record the Assemblage Point front and rear locations by marking the form with a pen on the front and rear of each of the three views of the man in the drawing. Then draw a line or arrow on each view. This will then give a clear indication of the entry angle and deviation angles. With time and experience, you will be able to acquire a deep understanding of the relationship between the location, entry angle and disease or symptoms. Keeping good records will allow you to review and improve your knowledge and techniques.

When you have shifted a patient's Assemblage Point, re-check their location and record this on the second part of the form. Record any comments which the patient may have, concerning how they now feel and be sure to record any physical or psychological changes that you observe. With a major Assemblage Point shift the patient's complexion, posture, facial expressions and other indicators invariably improve. It is useful to provide the patient with a mirror, so that they can see for themselves the visual improvements. Blood pressure, respiration and other medical factors, such as urine and blood analysis can be monitored. These will also show improvements after some time.

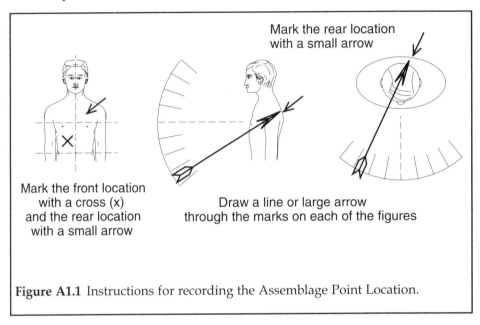

Figure A1.1 Instructions for recording the Assemblage Point Location.

At the bottom of the "Medical Analysis and Treatment Record Form" is a place for the patient to record a sample of their handwriting. This serves several purposes, the sample can be used for graphological analysis and the patient's psychological script and other factors can be determined. It also provides a paper record and a simple means of measuring the patient's muscle/brain coordinations. Where applicable, after treatment, the patient can give further samples to establish if there has been any improvement in their condition.

Where a patient is presenting serious or chronic health problems, physical examination is required to establish the cause of their disease. The form provides prompts and spaces to record any examination results.

Medical Analysis and Treatment Record Form

<u>Patient's Notes</u>

Date Time

Surname: First Names: Maiden Name:

Address:

Telephone No: Day: Evening:

Age: Date of Birth: Occupation:

Height: Weight: Marital Status:

Doctor: Address:

Specialist: Hospital:

Presenting:

Symptoms:

Allergies:

Medication and Therapies:

Surgical Operations:

Past Accidents Or Traumas:

Observation Notes:

Psychological Type: Introvert [　] Extrovert [　]

 Feeling [　] Intuitive [　] Practical [　] Rational [　]

Psychological Health: Unhealthy [　] Average [　] Healthy [　]

Physiological Type: Heavy [　] Medium [　] Light [　]

Examination Results and Notes:
Pulse and Blood Pressure:

Respiration:

Posture:

Complexion:

Liver:

Spleen:

Kidney Right:

Kidney Left:

Digestion Upper:

Digestion Lower:

Additional Comments:

Assemblage Point Location: Observations and Remarks:

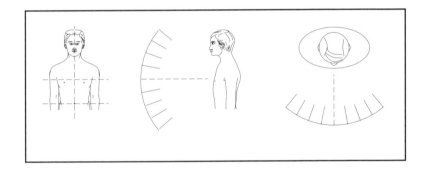

Gem Lamp Therapy Treatment Given:
1] Gems:	Area:	Filter:	Frequency:	Voltage:
2] Gems:	Area:	Filter:	Frequency:	Voltage:
3] Gems:	Area:	Filter:	Frequency:	Voltage:
4] Gems:	Area:	Filter:	Frequency:	Voltage:

Medications and Other Treatments Given:

Post Treatment Assemblage Point Location: Observations and Remarks:

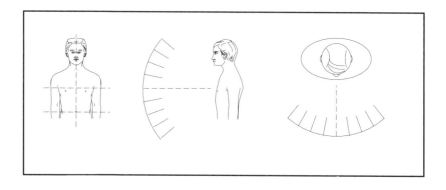

Recommendations:

Next Appointment: Date: Time:

Seen By: **At Location:**

HANDWRITING SAMPLE:- Please write in your normal handwriting
the following:- The quick brown fox jumps over the lazy dog. Please sign
your normal and familiar signatures.

Assemblage Point Correction Record Form

Date   Time _____

Surname: _____   First Names: _____

Address: _____

Age: _____   Date of Birth: _____   Occupation: _____

Height: _____   Weight: _____

Reason for Requiring Assemblage Point Correction:

Assemblage Point Location: Observations and Remarks:

Check the Location After Shifting: Observations and Remarks:

After Shifting; Comments, Remarks and Observations:

Seen By: _____   **At Location:** _____

ASSEMBLAGE POINT
SHIFTING CRYSTALS

Most large towns or cities will have shops which support the sale of quartz crystals. Rock and mineral shops, fancy gift shops and lapidary suppliers are just some of the outlets where crystals can be purchased. The prices will vary dramatically, but a large piece of rough unpolished quartz will only cost from £5 to perhaps £20. Polished and finished massage wands which would be suitable for shifting Assemblage Points will be substantially more expensive. Depending on the size, clarity and weight, the cost can vary from £30 to £100 or more. This is not so bad as only one is required and, provided that it is not dropped on to a hard floor, it should last indefinitely. Sometimes it is not possible to find a suitable polished crystal to do the job and one must be constructed from a rough specimen or you could get a jeweller to make one for you.

Through the late 1980's and 1990's, the author was running Assemblage Point training seminars and workshops. For these it was necessary to have a number of Assemblage Point shifting crystals at hand for participants to use. These were constructed from rough crystal by cutting off or grinding down the jagged end and shaping it into a convex, polished finish. The process is not difficult or too hazardous and there will be many engineers in a large town with both the equipment and skills necessary to do the job. For people who have difficulty in finding a suitable polished crystal, the procedures and equipment required to construct an Assemblage Point shifting crystal from rough crystal stock are listed below.

It is much easier to shift the Assemblage Point with a large powerful crystal. It is not that a smaller crystal will not work, the problem is that, when using smaller cheaper crystals, more of one's personal energy is

The minimum length should be not much less than 18 cm

The minimum diameter should be not much less than 3 cm

The minimum weight should be not much less than 200 grams

Figure A2.1 Specifications for Assemblage Point shifting quartz crystals.

required to achieve a shift. There are other problems. For example, if the crystal's diameter is too small, then it will be more difficult to place it precisely on the Assemblage Point location. Also, if the crystal is inactive or not large enough or sufficiently powerful, the Assemblage Point will not be arrested properly. In this case the crystal will let go of the patient's Assemblage Point during the process of shifting and the shift will be lost.

Bearing these factors in mind when purchasing a crystal will prevent disappointment. For consistent and easy shifting results, observe the following minimum standards for the crystal.

The crystal should weigh 200 gms or more, have a length of a least 18 cm and a diameter of 3 cm or more (that is over 10 cm in circumference). The crystal must have a ground and polished convex or domed end. It should be as clear as possible, have a well-defined point and the point should have at least three perfect triangles amongst its six facets (see Figure A2.1.).

How to Construct An Assemblage Point Shifter

The following instructions are for a competent engineer who has been trained to use a bench grinder and who is familiar with the safety precautions required. It is a very simple matter to grind and polish the dome shape on the end of a quartz crystal provided that one has the right tools. The process takes several hours and can be tedious but very rewarding and satisfying. A bench grinder similar to that shown in Figure A2.2. is required. The grinder's electrical installation should be approved by a qualified electrician. It must be properly earthed or grounded and connected to the mains supply via an earth leakage current breaker. Ideally it should be fitted with the following grinding and polishing wheels:

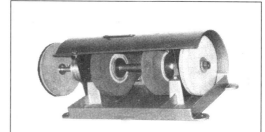

Figure A2.2 Lapidary grinder, sander, and polisher.

- 60 or 120 grit tungsten (Coarse green grit) grinding wheel.
- 120 or 220 grit tungsten (fine green grit) grinding wheel
- 1 x rubber backed sanding wheel.
- Hard felt padded polishing wheel.

When grinding quartz, it is essential to use a water coolant at all times, other wise the crystal will crack or break with the heat generated. This can easily be achieved with some plastic hose from a fish tank. To improvise the coolant, the following is required:

- 5 litre plastic water container
- 2 metres of 5 millimetre diameter clear flexible plastic tube or pipe (Pet shop, aquarium supplies).
- 1 small plastic tap to fit the plastic tube. (Pet shop aquarium supplies)
- Safety goggles for eye protection.

Arrange the coolant syphon so that the water container is supported about 10 or 20 centimetres above the grinder. Secure the plastic hose with the plastic tap in line, so that the water flow can be adjusted. Use a spring clothes peg to secure the coolant pipe to the grinder. Add a small quantity of washing up liquid to the water. Start the syphon, by sucking on the end of the pipe. Adjust and regulate the water flow so that the solution drips onto the surface of the grinding wheel. Do not use too much or too little coolant, it should drip at a rate of 1 to 3 drips each second. This will be a messy job, you will need a plastic apron and safety goggles to protect your eyes. The high speed rotation of the grinding wheel will throw the water out forwards.

Before starting work, use one layer of plastic bubble wrapping material to protect the crystal's pointed end. Wrap up the crystal tightly, leaving about 3 centimetres of the rough end exposed upon which you are going to work, and bind the wrapping with plastic insulation tape. This wrapping then acts as a very convenient handle to hold when grinding the crystal. It also gives the crystal some protection should you should accidentally bang or drop it.

Hold the crystal lightly but firmly against the course grit grinding wheel and rotate it just as you would when using a screwdriver. Keep the coolant dripping at all times. Continue to rotate and grind the crystal, until you have fashioned a dome or convex shape on the end as in Figure A2.1 above.

Then repeat this process using the fine grit grinding wheel. When you are satisfied with the shape and finish, all that is required is to polish it. Use contact adhesive to glue in sequence, 320, 400 and 600 grit wet and dry abrasive paper discs, to the rubber backed sanding wheel. The crystal is polished first with a 320 grit disk, then 400 and, finally, the finest grit of 600 is used. The wet and dry abrasive discs and the crystal must be kept wet with coolant at at times. Work through each grade until you achieve a fine finish, which is free of any scratches.

The final polish is given with the hard felt pad wheel. This should also be damp at all times and is best achieved with a plastic plant spraying bottle from the garden supply shop. Dampen the felt pad with spray and coat it with jeweller's rogue (ceric oxide). Then press and rotate the crystal against the revolving felt pad just as before. Using the spray bottle, constantly keep the pad damp, otherwise you will cause a blister crack on the domed surface. After a few minutes of work, the crystal will have a fine lustre.

Appendix III

THE BACKGROUND AND DEVELOPMENT OF ELECTRONIC GEM LAMP THERAPY

It is necessary to include here some details of apparatus and equipment used on patients. Those patients who received electronic gem lamp therapy described in the case studies throughout this book were treated with instruments designed and developed by the author. In most of the cases mentioned, the instruments used were either the Caduceus Lux III or the earlier design, Caduceus Lux II. Photographic details of both models are given below.

During the nineteen eighties and early nineties some patients and many private individuals received treatment with other types of instruments. Details of these have also been included below to indicate the lineage of research and development.

Hand Held Instruments

The hand held pocket sized instruments were developed in the nineteen eighties to treat minor health problems, such as cystitis, sciatica, back pain, shoulder pain, minor injuries, pre-menstrual tension, insomnia, migraine and various skin problems. These instruments were powered by either a six or a nine volt, dry battery (see Figure A3.1). They used an electronic transducer to excite the gem stones, this was attached to the instrument with a jack plug cable (see Figure A3.3). The transducer was

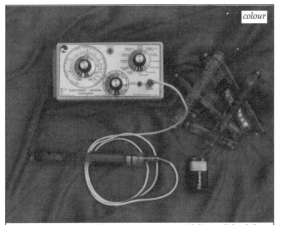

Figure A3.1 A battery powered hand held gem therapy instrument constructed and first built in 1985.

held in close proximity to the area of the body that required treatment. Unlike the Caduceus Lux II and III above, these instruments did not use coloured light; however, they were very effective for minor complaints.

These hand held instruments were not very suitable for use in a busy clinical practice, as the treatment time was too long and the patient would have to return several times for the therapy to be effective. However, they were very effective for personal use and they provided a great deal of positive research information and confirmation. Figure A3.2 shows the front panel drawing of the instrument; the larger dial was calibrated on the outer scale with brain frequencies. The output power was very small at only a few thousandths of a watt.

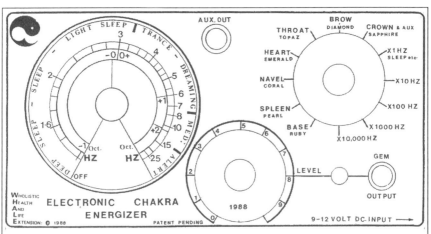

Figure A3.2 The front panel drawing showing the large dial calibrated with brain frequencies.

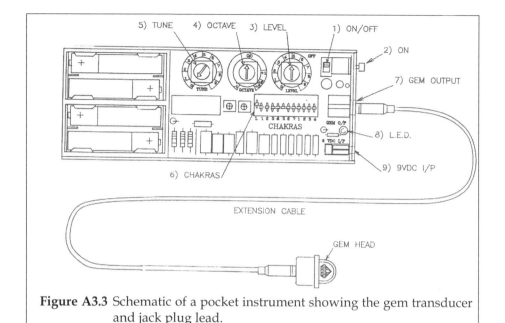

Figure A3.3 Schematic of a pocket instrument showing the gem transducer and jack plug lead.

Caduceus Lux I

This was the prototype of the first instruments to combine the use of gem stones and coloured light with electronic modulation of the gem stones. Only three were built from around 1990 onwards (see Figure A3.4). This instrument was designed to meet the increasing demand caused by patients with problematic or serious conditions seeking electronic gem therapy treatment. The original impetus came about in an attempt to find a treatment for jaw bone infection and other serious health problems caused by filling of the root canals in teeth (see Figure A3.6). The prototype lamps were constructed from hard wood with in-built lenses and electronic gem transducers. The lamps and electronic instrumentation were powered by a separate safe 12 volts D.C.

Figure A3.4 The first clinical instrument that combined the use of colour, light and electronically excited gem stones.

power supply. The instrument included dual channels and digital frequency and treatment level indicators. The lamps in the beginning were hand held and the wooden finish was warm to the skin. The lamps were held close to or actually touching the skin. The photograph Figure A3.4 shows a box of gem stones, wooden lamp and cable, together with the electronic control unit. As many as four lamps could be driven by this instrument.

The equipment was very popular and successful and patients enjoyed the personal attention it gave them. After some months the clinic therapists got tired of holding lamps close to patients. It caused the therapists fatigue and repetitive strain. It was also a waste of time, as it prevented them from keeping the patient's records, making notes, or performing other duties. The wooden lamps were later fitted with adjustable floor stands (see Figure A3.5). This instrument was used to establish the parameters and calibration of the lamps, frequencies, quantities and sizes of gem, the treatment levels, times and duration of treatments for a comprehensive range of diseases and symptoms. During this period new lamp designs were in hand and the wooden prototype lamps were replaced with higher powered lamps constructed and machined in metal (see Figure A3.10 on page 189).

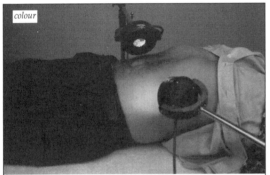

Figure A3.5 Irritable bowel syndrome under treatment with wooden lamps.

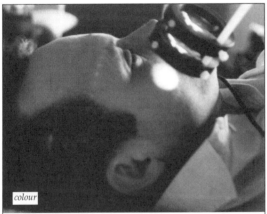

Figure A3.6 Experimental lamps used to treat iatrogenic dental problems.

The treatments and therapies were restricted to the following combinations of gems and colour filters used in the lamps:

• VIOLET LAMPS filled with sapphires vibrating at slow

Delta and Theta brain frequencies are used to calm, relax, pacify nerves, tissue, muscles, organs or endocrine glands. Commonly used for pain associated with nerve damage and irritation, sciatica, post injury and surgical trauma, anxiety, shock, stress, phobias, addiction, emotional trauma, emotional and physical exhaustion, psoriasis.

• GREEN LAMPS filled with emeralds and blue sapphires are used to cool and pacify nerves, tissue, muscles, organs or endocrine glands. They are used for burns, new injuries, inflammation and soreness, dermatitis, eczema, digestion and gastric conditions, all conditions where cellular activity and heat are too high.

• ORANGE LAMPS filled with carnelians and diamonds are used to increase biological energy, activity and circulation in tissue, muscles, organs or endocrine glands. They are used for eczema, oedema, varicose ulcers, circulation and various blood conditions, numbness and muscular atrophy, cartilage and disc problems, under active organs and glands. Most often used with elderly patients, as they increase biological energy.

This instrument was in very good service for almost two years, when one day, whilst the author was treating a patient he tripped on one of the lamp cables laying on the floor and the whole instrument got pulled off the trolley with a crash. The instrument was just too light for serious clinical application and this embarrassment led to an immediate redesign and the birth of the Caduceus Lux II and III.

Caduceus Lux II and III

The technical specifications for both models are about the same, but the instrument front panel layout is considerably different. Both models have digital readouts which indicate the treatment levels and frequency rate. However, in a clinical situation, patients can be distractive and this could interfere with the process of adjusting knobs to set the values for the patient's treatment and errors could occur, so the Caduceus Lux II

Figure A3.7 An instrument with automatic treatment selection, Caduceus Lux III.

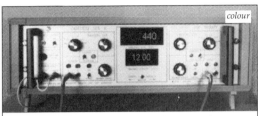

colour

Figure A3.8 A dual channel manual instrument, Caduceus Lux II.

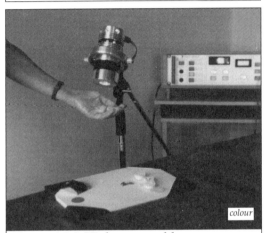

colour

Figure A3.9 High powered lamps machined from metal.

(Figure A3.8.) was phased out and replaced by the Caduceus Lux III (Figure A3.7). This instrument incorporated 'coloured illuminated push buttons' switches for treatment selection and the switch colours matched the lamp colours. This eliminated the possibility of errors and the tediousness of turning or adjusting knobs, permitting the therapist to give full attention to the patient. The Caduceus Lux III design incorporates over a decade of practical clinical experience treating patients with energy medicine. There has been ample time, plenty of pragmatic experience and sufficient critical analysis of previous instruments and therapies to produce a robust and ergonomically sound design which almost anyone can use in any situation.

The Electronic Caduceus

The origins of the author's involvement in the design of the gem therapy equipment started in the seventies. The Caduceus is the ancient Greek emblem, often used as a logo by various members of the medical and dental profession, and it is also the name of a popular alternative and complementary health magazine. Very few people are aware of the medical significance of the Caduceus symbol or why for centuries it has had associations with the medical profession. The Staff of Mercury was made of gold, with two snakes entwined around it and at the top of the staff are two golden wings like an eagles. The Greek story about the origins of the Caduceus is interesting: The golden staff was given to the messenger of the gods, who was called Mercury by the king of the gods, Jupiter. It is said that the Caduceus has the power over sleep, dreams, wealth and happiness. This is not the only reason why for centuries, it has been used as a logo by the medical profession.

Indian, Tibetan and, to some extent Chinese traditional medicine, refer to seven biological energy meridians, called chakras. Great importance is placed on these seven chakras as they are associated with the functions of seven major glands and organs of the body. There are also three major channels which distribute pranic or chi energy and kundalini energy to the chakras. These three important channels are often represented in ancient Indian medical text and paintings as two snakes entwined around the spine. There are currently thousands of books and publications which give very detailed references and accounts of the effects of these chakras. Great emphasis is placed on them and their importance for health, vitality and personal spiritual development. Some alternative and complementary therapies involve energising and balancing the patient's seven chakras by massage, acupuncture, colour therapy and other methods. Most of the current published material concerning the chakras and chi energy and so on is largely of a mystical or esoteric nature. Unfortunately, very little scientific research or study has been carried out to establish if these energy meridians exist or indeed what effect they have on our health.

Several scientific research instruments were designed and constructed for the purpose of energising the seven chakras (see Figure A3.10 and A3.11.). These were called the Electronic Caduceus. As things turned out, these instruments were extremely effective and they rapidly renewed biological energy, increased personal vitality and induced profound feelings of contentment and pleasure. It was also established at that time that regular treatment significantly improved health and increased resistance against common

colour

Figure A3.10
The Electronic Caduceus.

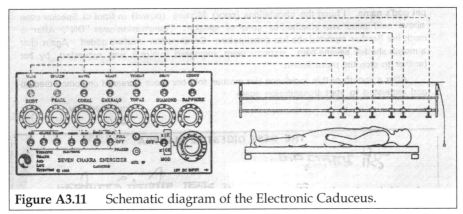

Figure A3.11   Schematic diagram of the Electronic Caduceus.

infections, such as colds or influenza. These instruments provided the basic hypothesis for the medical application of electronic gem lamp therapy and they were the forerunners of the current clinical instruments.

Caduceus Lux III Specifications

1) Caduceus Lux III is completely safe, the Lamps are 12 volt DC types. The lamps are fitted with ultra violet and infra red filters. The light beam is cool as the infra red heat spectrum is filtered out. The main instrument will drive up to three lamps at the same time, which enables treatment to multiple sites or large areas. Adjustable stands allow the lamps to target any area of the body.

2) Bright red and green digital displays permit the practitioner to monitor the treatment intensity and the vibrational rate, or frequency. The therapy frequency can be set to any desired value from 1.5 to 25,000 cycles per second. Treatment intensity can be adjusted according to the patient's sensitivity or age. The therapy intensity control is adjustable from zero to 12 .5 volts.

3) The Caduceus Lux III is housed in heavy duty, medical equipment casing. The size of the case is Width = 530 mm, Height = 170 mm, Depth = 330 mm. Instrument weight = 10 Kg. Fitted with tilt feet. Operates from any mains 90 - 270 volt AC, 50 to 60 Hz, wall socket. Europe or USA.

4) The Caduceus Lux III Lamps are fitted with special, long-life bulbs which emit a broad spectrum of light. The light beam is cool and is filtered and focussed through lenses. The lamp can be unscrewed to enable the gems and coloured filters to be changed. The lamps are precision

engineered from high quality materials. Lamp stands are made of high quality steel and are finished in chrome and matt black. The complete lamp and stand weight is 3.3 Kg.

5) Lamps can be supplied pre-filled with gem stones to suit practitioners' requirements. For a system with two lamps, the following quantities of gem stones are provided in a black leatherette display box with ten transparent compartments. The practitioner can select and place these in the Lamps to suit the patient's needs. The gems supplied for two lamps are: Ruby (6), Carnelian (18), Citrine (6), Emerald (12), Yellow Sapphire (6), Diamond (12), Blue Sapphire (12). Calibrated sets of coloured filters:- Red, Orange, Yellow, Green, Blue, Indigo, Violet. Others are available.

Caduceus Lux III is manufactured in Great Britain to British Standards MQIA ISO 9001 by:

WHALE MEDICAL
PO Box 31
Seaton
Devon
EX12 2YB
United Kingdom

Email: info@whalemedical.com

Please understand that it can be difficult and unethical to give medical advice by telephone or email. More imprtantly, your confidentiality may be breached as it cannot be guaranteed that such communications are strictly private. It is not practical or advisable to give any recommendations for treatment without a medical interview and examination. Your health could be put at risk if you are not given correct and proper attention, which is generally not possible by telephone, email or letter. Please see the following Internet web pages for the latest information.

Websites: whalemedical.com
Also see: theassemblagepoint.com

Compromising Patients' Health For Profit

Patients with chronic health problems are disadvantaged and are easily influenced and manipulated. Some medical doctors or enthusiastic professional therapists will always refer patients on, if they are unable to solve their problem, but this is unfortunately not always the case.

A lady reported in to the clinic accompanied by a friend. Her symptoms were panic, anxiety, diarrhoea, irritable bowels, palpitations, eczema and vertigo. These symptoms had developed after she contracted a virulent influenza virus in the autumn of the previous year. She had been experiencing these symptoms for some five months and was attending an alternative and complementary clinic during this period. She was taking the numerous vitamin and mineral supplements, together with other alternative medications and therapies which this clinic had prescribed and sold to her. However, her condition and symptoms had continued to deteriorate. The patient was given a physical examination and the initial suspected diabetes diagnosis was confirmed with a blood and urine analysis.

This patient, who had not been to see her doctor, was referred to the hospital. This type of occurrence is all too frequent. Any medical doctor would have taken one look at this patient and have immediately ordered a sample analysis of the patient's blood glucose levels and referred her to a hospital. Diabetes is a life threatening disease, the patient can go into a coma whilst driving or perhaps operating machinery, or when they are at home alone. Diabetics often wear a special bracelet, so that in the event of an ambulance being called, the attending paramedics are warned of the condition.

The National Health Service generally only uses medications and therapies that have been evaluated with scientific trials whereas most alternative and complementary medicines or therapies have not been subjected to any scientific analysis. Hardly a week passes without a new type of therapy, dietary supplements, herbal cure-alls appearing in the press or on some TV programme. There are always those willing to exploit those who are ill and those who are, genuinely, seeking to help them. On many occasions I have had to listen to patients' indignant remarks and lamentations concerning the suffering and fortunes spent on the numerous alternative therapies and medications which they had been prescribed or undertaken. Patients can avoid incidents or situations like the ones mentioned by consulting the following check list. These questions are useful to prompt or stimulate analytical thinking and common sense.

Check List For Patients

• Have you received a medical examination, had tests, for example, for blood pressure, or have urine or blood samples, scans or x-rays been taken?
• Has your ailment or condition been properly diagnosed?
• Is the diagnosis the root cause of your symptoms, or is it simply the name of the particular symptoms or disease that you have?
• How long have you been ill?
• Is the therapy on offer simply addressing your symptoms, or is it addressing the root cause of your health problem?
• Does the therapy have a well established and proven track record of success for your particular disease or symptoms?
• What are the known side effects?
• What is the success rate in percentages for different age groups?
• Is the success percentage higher than the official placebo effect levels of between 30% and 70%?
• How many treatments are you likely to have to receive before seeing progress?
• If a course of medication or therapeutic measures are being recommended, how many weeks will it take to address your condition?
• If the course of treatment proposed will take several weeks or months to treat you, is there a chance that your condition is likely to get better of its own accord within this time?
• How long will each treatment last?
• Will the treatment be stressful or even painful?

• Will you enjoy the experience and feel confident about its effects or will you endure the treatment in the hope it will do good?
• Does the clinic or practitioners have the necessary equipment and other means to make an accurate diagnosis?
• Can the clinic or therapist provide laboratory analysis of samples?
• Is the practitioner insured and qualified to practice the particular therapy that he is offering you?
• How much practical or clinical medical experience does he or she have?
• Are adequate patient records being kept?
• Are the medications that the practitioner supplies from a licensed manufacturer?
• How can you be sure that any medicines prescribed are authentic; what kind of quality assurance controls does the supplier use and who is the official authority overseeing their quality assurance?
• Is the therapeutic equipment being used by the practitioner safe?

Check List For Therapists

Approximately five or perhaps ten percent of my correspondence involves alternative practitioners enquiring about the validity and effectiveness of other manufacturers' equipment or products. On one occasion a therapist booked an appointment and turned up with a small hand-held electronic instrument which she had paid £1750 for. This instrument is applied by the therapist holding it onto the patient's skin. She asked, "Do you understand how it works?" I replied, "Yes, it works on the same principles as medical T.E.N.S. instruments used for pain relief, they cost about £100". She became antagonistic so, to settle the matter, I went to the cupboard and got out a T.E.N.S. instrument along with an electronic oscilloscope. She was very disappointed when she observed on the display screen of the oscilloscope that both the expensive and the cheap instrument produced identical electrical outputs.

It is very difficult to make a scientific evaluation of the vast numbers of health products which are currently appearing. In this respect, the following check list of points will be found helpful.

• Exactly what and how many diseases and symptoms will the product treat?
• How effective is it?
• What is the success rate for the product in percentages for different age groups?

• Is the success percentage higher than the official placebo effect levels of between 30% and 70%?
• What will the patient experience physically, mentally and emotionally?
• Will the patient enjoy the therapy?
• How many treatments are needed?
• How long does each treatment take?
• How will the product be applied to solve the patient's problems?
• How are you going to apply the product or device to your patient's problem?
• Will you or a therapist have to stand for long periods holding a piece of equipment on the patient?
• How many weeks will it take before you and your staff get fed up with personally using time and energy to hold an instrument on a patient?
• Will using the equipment give a therapist repetitive strain injury of any kind?
• How busy is the clinic and can a therapist be spared to be with a patient throughout treatment with certain types of equipment?
• Will the product fit in with a high turnover of patients?
• Is the equipment sufficiently safe for the patient to be left unattended while you answer the phone or take a tea break or see another patient in another room or perform other essential tasks, such as compiling patient records?
• What happens if the patient receives too much exposure?
• How much exposure will you and your staff receive?
• How will this affect you?
• Is the equipment versatile and easy to use, without complex training?
• How much risk of error is there in using the equipment?
• What track record does the equipment have?
• Will you have to consult complicated sets of instructions or frequency tables and set up the instrument for each of your patients?
• What will happen if a mistake is made in the setting of the instrument's controls?
• How can you be sure that the equipment is functioning correctly?
• How will you know if the equipment output is not faulty?
• Can the patient come to harm if the wrong treatment given?
• With electronic diagnostic equipment, how can you be sure that the readings you are taking are accurate?
• When was the equipment last inspected and calibrated?
• Is the equipment licensed and what is the track record of the manufacturing company?

• When, where and how much research has been done on the effectiveness and safety of the product?
• How valid is the scientific research material available concerning the product?
• Who is behind the design and research?
• What do you get for your money in terms of hardware, training, calibration and service?
• How robust and durable is the product and what is its expected service life?
• How many are there and what is the cost of the consumables?

Deceptions, Exploitations and Pretenses

Here are four examples of how easily patients are mislead by unethical practices, contrived talk, advertising and propaganda.

A male patient had attended the clinic once or twice each year for Assemblage Point correction in connection with his drinking. His home was some 200 miles from the clinic and this was a difficulty. However, he responded to an advert for Assemblage Point shifting which he found in a health magazine placed by a therapist much closer to his home. He attended his appointment but was disappointed to discover that the therapist had no idea of how to locate and shift Assemblage Points. The therapist did a number of odd things to him, told him that his Assemblage Point was now corrected and presented his bill. The patient telephoned us later the same day and booked an appointment. As soon as he arrived late the next afternoon, the nurse confirmed that his Assemblage Point was not to be found in the centre but it was located twelve centimetres below his right nipple.

On another occasion, a shy introvert lady patient had travelled 280 miles to the clinic for treatment for chronic depression. Her Assemblage Point was corrected. On her second visit the patient was very much better and more talkative. She complained to the nurse that her London alternative doctor had three months previously supplied her with an expensive course of herbal medications that had not worked. She said that, when she asked him about the Assemblage Point and her depression, he told her that it caused cancer. This was not an isolated incident, several other reports came into the offices which substantiated her story. This particular alternative practitioner was on our files and was very well aware of the benefits of Assemblage Point therapy for depression, as he was fully conversant with the relating published papers and case studies.

A young male patient had previously spent three months having hypnotherapy and psychotherapy for his psoriasis. He had suffered this on and off since childhood. He told the attending nurse that he thought that the hypnotherapy had helped a little. The nurse said, "Let's have a look at you". He showed her his legs, which were covered in scabs, bleeding and had cracked skin which was badly infected from his knees downwards. He was asked if he had been to see his doctor, to which he replied, "I do not trust the medicines they prescribe because it always comes back worse each time". The nurse told him that he must go to his doctor immediately as he required hospital treatment.

There is a more humourous side to alternative medicine and the following email was received from a female doctor:

". . . coincidently, last week I saw a 'phone in' health programme. The programme presenters and their guest, an alternative practitioner, were surrounded by baskets of different coloured vegetables complete with a backdrop of rainbow coloured curtains. It was not clear whether this was a cooking programme, a fashion show or a medical programme. As the programme continued with people phoning in for advice, it became evident that it was a combined cooking/fashion/medical programme! The alternative practitioner gave the telephoning viewers his recommendations and advice for various symptoms or complaints. For PMT, he gave a list of the seven different colours of the clothes women should wear and the colour of the fruits and vegetables they should eat during the seven days leading up to their period.

Most women have little precise prior knowledge about when their period will begin. Even those on the contraceptive pill cannot know exactly which day will be the fourth, fifth or sixth day before their period. The normal female cycle can vary by up to a fortnight from the 28 day lunar cycle. Therefore, for a man to blithely tell women what to wear or eat on which day is totally ridiculous and very suspicious.

Even if it were possible to predict with any degree of accuracy, what woman would want to proclaim to the world she was four days away from her period by wearing bright yellow from head to foot and spend the day eating bananas, lemons, yellow courgettes and custard! She would look and feel at the least very foolish and at worst self-conscious and even ill. There is also a limit to the amount of blue food anyone could consume in a day - how would this man like to spend a day eating red cabbage, beetroot, blackberries and blueberries? Only a mercenary, very unintelligent and egocentric man could suggest this to women...."

Appendix V

Scientific Validation of the Assemblage Point and Electronic Gem Lamp Therapy

If today's scientific models prove inadequate, it is because tomorrow's will be better. In the nineteen sixties and seventies many scientific researchers independently established the fact that, during ordinary states of consciousness, the brain's electrical activity in the left hemisphere was greater than that in the right hemisphere. The same researchers established that, with the help of feedback from electroencephalogram (EEG) recordings and other types of electronic devices which monitored brain electrical activity, subjects were able to slow down their brain frequencies by reducing their thinking activities. When the subject reduced his brain frequencies to between 7.0 and 13.0 cycles per second, the EEG recorder displayed electrical coherence of the left and right brain hemispheres. The subjects commonly reported subjective feelings of peacefulness, centeredness and light. From these studies it was generally concluded that the larger electrical activity of the left hemisphere was generated by the process of thinking, that is, that our thought processing takes place in the left hemisphere. However, this is an assumption. Scientifically it cannot be demonstrated that the left brain's electrical activity is produced by our thoughts. There is now new evidence to suggest that this electrical activity is not produced by the process of thinking.

Back in nineteen sixty, when I was still at school, I constructed a simple electronic brain monitor which was worn on the head. It consisted of a very sensitive electronic transistor amplifier in a screened metal box, which was fixed to a metal head band along with a pair of ex-Royal Air Force war-time headphones. The head band was equipped with four spring loaded electrodes made from two copper halfpennies. When the headband was placed on the head, the spring loaded electrodes made contact with each side of the head. The transistor amplifier amplified the brain's frequencies so that the wearer could hear his own brain activity via the headphones. Using this device, it was easy to achieve states of profound meditation. It proved very popular amongst my contemporaries at school and it survived for about two weeks before it was confiscated by one of my teachers. It was eventually thrown into the school's water heating furnace by the caretaker on the orders of the headmaster during one of the regular burning rituals of several dozens of packets of confiscated cigarettes! I was disappointed as transistors were expensive and not easy to come by in those days and I learnt at a very young age to keep my enthusiastic scientific projects away from the public gaze. I also discovered that enthusiasm and truth can be easily destroyed by covert and overt hostility.

The Placebo Trial

Over the years I have spent hundreds of hours investigating the electrical properties of the Assemblage Point and I have made even more experiments on myself using electronic gem therapy lamps. All of the treatment procedures which I have designed were in the first place tried out on myself. I would not subject any patient to a treatment which I had not first given to myself, even though I did not have their diseases or symptoms.

For example, some years ago, when I had occasion to treat a young child who was covered from head to toes with eczema, I performed a series of controlled experiments testing the effect of the electronic gem therapy lamps on the electrical conductivity of my skin. The results were very interesting and presented conclusive scientific evidence of the benefits of electronic gem lamp therapy for controlling and treating disease. The experiment was set up to prove the effectiveness of electronic gem therapy lamps containing rubies for increasing local circulation of the dermis and emerald for reducing circulation in the dermis. The placebo control was ordinary "colour therapy" lamps and the same lamps and filters were used for the control, but without gem stones fitted inside them. This experiment was very similar to the temperature measuring experiment in Figure 6.4 and Figure 6.5 in Chapter 6. Furthermore, the following experiment substantiated the results of that test. The details of the experiment are as follows:

1) I marked off two areas of my left forearm with a fine marker pen as area 'A' and area 'B'.

2) Inside the centre of the area, I measured the skin resistance of both sites 'A' and 'B', using a calibrated ohmmeter with gold contact skin probes attached. The distance between the probes was fixed at 2 centimetres. These readings were:

Site 'A' = 52,000,000 ohms
Site 'B' = 47,000,000 ohms.

3) Area 'A' was treated for five minutes with the red placebo control lamp.

4) Area 'B' was simultaneously treated with the second red lamp containing 6 rubies of a size of 6 x 8 millimetres. The frequency used to stimulate the rubies was 8.3 HZ.

5) After five minutes of treatment the readings were taken again as follows:

Site 'A' = 83,000,000 ohms
Site 'B' = 27,000,000 ohms.

The results showed that the site treated by the colour therapy placebo red lamp had increased by 31,000,000 ohms and the site treated by ruby had decreased by 20,000,000 ohms.

I was surprised to discover and prove that the placebo lamp actually increased the electrical resistance of the dermis by drying it out. Whereas the gem therapy lamp containing rubies decreased the skin resistance by stimulating circulation, bringing blood and body fluids closer to the surface of the skin.

Twenty minutes later, the same experiment was carried out on my right arm using a green placebo lamp and a second green lamp filled with 6 emeralds as above.

Skin resistance before treatment was:

Site 'A' = 23,000,000 ohms.
Site 'B' = 28,000,000 ohms.

Skin resistance after treatment was:

Site 'A' = 24,000,000 ohms.
Site 'B' = 57,000,000 ohms.

The result showed that the site treated by the colour therapy placebo green lamp had increased by only 1,000,000 ohms and the site treated with the emerald lamp had increased by 29,000,000 ohms.

This experiment demonstrated that the placebo green colour therapy lamp did not dry out the skin as much as the red placebo colour therapy lamp above. It demonstrated and proved that the green lamp containing emeralds decreased the local circulation and moisture content of the dermis.

These two simple and inexpensive experiments scientifically proved the effectiveness of electronic gem therapy lamps. What emerald and ruby lamps can do to the skin, they can also do to internal organs. Green emerald lamps will reduce overheated and swollen tissue or organs and red ruby lamps can increase the activity of cold contracted tissue and organs.

They also proved that ordinary colour therapy lamps, when compared to electronic gem therapy lamps, have an opposite effect and can have an adverse reaction for some conditions. This is in fact the case. Some time after this I was asked by a hospital skin specialist to conduct a series of placebo trails in his hospital's skin ward. The specialist wanted to use ordinary colour therapy lamps as the placebo. Before agreeing, I made a pilot trial in my own clinic based on the specialist's requirements. When patients' skin problems were treated with ordinary colour therapy lamps, these aggravated the condition. I eventually declined to do the trial, as I was not prepared to treat volunteers with a placebo therapy which would make their symptoms worse.

The Assemblage Point Acid Test

I have tried numerous experiments on myself to try to obtain a reliable and repeatable electronic method to scientifically prove the existence of the Assemblage Point. I have taken thousands of readings over the area of my chest and back using various types of sensitive electronic measuring equipment. I have been able to prove to my personal satisfaction that there is a measurable distinction in the area of the Assemblage Point location. Ordinarily, a clinician may present his or her cases with the expectation that they will be accepted at face value, although the conclusions may be questioned. I am aware of the scientific limitations of my experiments and have hesitated in recording them here but I feel that holding back data is evasive and, in the long run, destructive to the progress of science.

I feel that the following data is of sufficient importance that, when it is confirmed by other researchers, it will create a new paradigm of medical treatment and the prevention of disease. For as soon as the medical profession is provided with conclusive evidence from a wide body of researchers of the dangerous consequences for patients' with a misaligned Assemblage Point, it will be unethical if they do nothing about it.

Recently my own findings have been confirmed independently by a British physicist. Much earlier in the year, I had been treating a patient incapacitated with a serious degenerative condition with electronic gem therapy lamp treatment and Assemblage Point correction.This patient made a rapid recovery after only three treatment sessions. Unknown to me, the patient was cooperating with the physicist. The physicist's laboratory was full of sensitive electronic equipment which he used to measure the energy levels of organs and glands for diagnostic purposes. On the way to my clinic for treatment, the patient called into the physicist's lab for various tests and measurements. After receiving electronic gem lamp treatment for the liver and spleen, the patient would return to the physicist's laboratory for more tests and measurements. The physicist's tests and measurements proved beyond doubt that electronic gem lamp therapy and Assemblage Point correction was making a profound improvement to the patient's biological energies. The physicist's electrical measurements and readings substantiated the progress of this patient's physical and psychological recovery throughout that period of treatment.

This was important research data and had profound implications for medical science so a meeting was arranged to which I was invited. Recently, a research team gathered at the physicist's laboratory and the electronic gem therapy lamps were tested on the patient with a liver condition. The physicist made a series of measurements on the patient before, during and after treatment and the results were recorded.

When the hospital doctor monitors a patient's heart beat with an electrocardiogram recorder the signal level for an adult is around 1000 micro-volts and, for a pregnant mother, the foetal heart beat signal is only 50 micro-volts, but in this case the signal is alternating current and therefore has a frequency component. Unlike the measurement of the body's frequencies such as brain waves or the heart beat, normally, I would not pay much credence to any type of diagnostics based on the electrical measurements of the skin. Measuring the skin and signals upon it is very unreliable as skin resistance can vary from one person to another and the value of between several million ohms to only a few thousand ohms can be recorded. The values vary wildly according to emotional circumstances, the ambient temperature, weather conditions and thousands of other factors. Further, unless great care is exercised, the amount of pressure applied when taking electrical skin readings can affect the results by several hundred percent, as can, say, drinking a cup of tea. Therefore, it is impossible to get an accurate, calibrated reading with high impedance measuring devices and it is impossible to establish a data base line of a sufficient number of different healthy people from which a scientific model can be constructed.

The physicist had developed a technique of measuring the body's electrical activities using two special probes connected to a sensitive low impedance laboratory mirror galvanometer. He had spent some years developing the special probes with non-polarising porous electrodes. The probes were filled with a salt water solution of a strength equal to that of the human body and they made wet contact with the skin. At high energy areas and points on the skin, ionic exchange takes place and this is recorded by the galvanometer. The fact that a low input impedance galvanometer was being used was reassuring for my scepticism. This was very reassuring as it reduced the chance of errors being caused by background noise and other electrical interference.

Without being specific, the patient had a hot and agitated diseased liver condition and the liver readings at times could be in the order of 30 to 50 times higher than those of a healthy person. The patient's liver readings before treatment were recorded at 30 micro-volts. After five minutes of treatment with a cooling, calming, slow frequency gem therapy lamp containing emeralds and blue sapphires, the patient's liver readings were taken again and they had reduced to 20 micro-volts. At the end of a twenty minute treatment session, the patient's liver readings had reduced to a value of 12 micro-volts, which represents a decrease of 60 percent.

This patient also confirmed that, when the liver readings were high and the liver was upset, the quality of thought processing became agitated and angry. In addition, it was noted by those present that electronic gem lamp therapy to the liver had rapidly improved the quality of the patient's mood and complexion and demonstrated how imbalances in the functions of organs can affect and dominate not only physical appearance but, also, psychological moods. Adjusting the energy levels of imbalanced organs makes a profound improvement on a patient's psychological state.

Everyone present, including the patient, agreed that the electronic gem lamp therapy validated and supported the measuring techniques and that the measuring techniques confirmed the profound and rapid effect of the of the electronic gem lamp therapy. We quickly moved on to measure the Assemblage Point.

The editor of this book, Dr. Angela Blaen, a Research Fellow at Exeter University, volunteered to have her Assemblage Point measured and the results using the physicist's special probes were as impressive as those obtained on the patient's liver. The Assemblage Point location was located in the normal way both at the front of the chest and on the back. The volunteer was familiar with her Assemblage Point location and confirmed that it had been located correctly. The skin was marked with a pen on the chest and on the back with a small circle of 2 centimetres in diameter around the location.

Using one probe on the chest and one on the volunteer's back, the physicist took a series of measurements (see Figure A5.1). At first he applied his probes on the skin. The readings outside of the two centimetre circles were on average 10 micro-volts. When he applied the probes to the skin in the centre of the circle, the location of the Assemblage Point, the galvanometer needle registered 50 micro-volts, an increase of 500 percent.

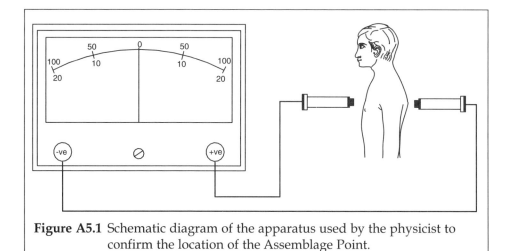

Figure A5.1 Schematic diagram of the apparatus used by the physicist to confirm the location of the Assemblage Point.

Two weeks after this meeting, using my own apparatus, I repeated and confirmed the Assemblage Point measurements using the ionic transfer current probes developed by the physicist. A nurse located and marked the position of my Assemblage Point and she applied the probes and the readings were 20 - 30 micro-volts outside of the circle and 180 -200 micro-volts on the location. The reason for the readings being higher than those recorded by the physicist is that I used a low impedance electronic differential operational amplifier to boost the signal from the probes.

I have to make it clear that scientifically we do not know what it is that is being measured and these procedures cannot be used to locate the Assemblage Point. However, they are useful for confirming the location. As yet no readings have been taken on patients with pathological Assemblage Point locations and it is now an urgent matter to measure as many patients as possible to build up a data base of voltages associated with different diseases.

The powerful and rapid curative effects of Assemblage Point correction therapy and electronic gem lamp therapy can be evaluated not only by the obvious and subjective results experienced by the patient but also by analysing the disease or symptoms being treated and by applying the following standard scientific methods:

- Laboratory blood analysis
- Laboratory urine analysis
- Laboratory swab testing
- Blood pressure and heart rate monitoring
- Electrocardiograms
- Temperature measurement
- Skin conductivity measurement
- Infra red photography and image scanning
- Electronic measurement of reflex and muscle/motor coordination
- Electronic measurement of nervous system voltages and currents.
- Electroencephalograms
- Ultrasonic scanning
- X-Ray imagery and scanning
- Medical psychological examination, testing and evaluation
- Medical physiological examination, testing and evaluation

Unlike almost all other therapeutic modalities, both Assemblage Point correction therapy and electronic gem lamp therapy adjust, change, increase or decrease the biological energy of the patient. Therefore, the benefits of these therapies take place as the therapy is given. These benefits can be monitored, measured and confirmed as the therapy proceeds, or immediately after treatment.

Currently there is a research project proposed at Exeter University to record the numerous voltage readings of sixty healthy volunteers. This is required to establish a base line of values from which to work. With such a data base it would be possible to measure the electrical energy of patients' organs, glands and other areas of their body and intercept disease before it manifests as physical damage. Common diseases such as arthritis, rheumatism, back pain, oedema, migraine, heart conditions, cancer, diabetes, Parkinsonism, etc, all give much higher readings than are obtained with a normal healthy person. Electronic gem lamp therapy, as opposed to drug therapy, can reduce these voltages quickly and the medical benefits for patients has been adequately demonstrated throughout this book.

The liver is a large organ on the right side of the body and all right handed parts of the body are controlled by feedback signalling pathways to the left brain hemisphere. One of the many factors that has surfaced as a result of these tests is that psychological symptoms associated with excessive left brain electrical activity can be substantially reduced by treatment to calm and cool the patient's liver. Under stressful situations the liver is called on to supply the body and brain with glucose and other nutrients. From this perspective was the left brain's electrical activity measured by those early researchers due to the process of human thinking or were they actually measuring the brain-to-liver signalling traffic?

Our current physiological, psychological and spiritual models for Homo Sapiens, in the light of the discoveries outlined and proved in this book, are now obviously out of date and inadequate. Urgent research is required by all relevant departments in our universities and medical teaching establishments to update and include these discoveries into our current operating models.

Appendix VI

Science — The Concluding Resolution

Most medical doctors who I know, and probably many more whom I do not know, consider alternative and complementary medicine to be bordering on quackery or at best "supportive therapy". However, there is one subject that almost all doctors will agree upon and that is electromagnetic therapy. Medical doctors and hospitals would never employ electromagnetic therapy for their patients, due to the risks of damage or inducing iatrogenic disease to patients and interfering with other electronic medical equipment close by. Hospitals do not permit the use of mobile telephones inside their buildings for exactly this reason. Furthermore, there is very little medical evidence to suggest that electromagnetic radiation has any therapeutic properties and all of the evidence suggests that it is dangerous as it induces biological stress and damage by inducing electrical eddy currents and voltages into living tissue which is conductive and very sensitive. From this perspective hardly a week passes without some report of the dangers and risks occurring in the media and there are currently a number of affected people suing for compensation.

Electromagnetic therapy has a dubious history, even involving outright fraud with very few serious attempts to evaluate the effects of oscillating or static magnetic fields to cure diseases. One alternative practitioner equipped his chain of clinics with a number of electronic gem lamp therapy systems and promptly renamed the therapy as his own "Electromagnetic Light Therapy". After some months of success by his staff of treating patients, he went on television to demonstrate his use of the lamps and told viewers that it was electromagnetic light therapy. A number of therapists who use electronic gem lamp therapy and saw the programme, naturally got very upset and complained to a several government departments who later advised the practitioner that he was breaking the law. Other writers have referred to electronic gem lamp therapy incorrectly as colour therapy and coloured light therapy. One author stated in a recent book Light from the Caduceus Lux III (electronic gem lamp therapy) has the power to shine right through the skull or chest..., which of course is nonsense and it is small wonder that medical doctors adopt the views mentioned above when the reading this type of material.

There are many books currently in print or about to be published, in which the authors have included a section about my research and development work. Indeed, some authors have quoted from my work 'word for word' and others have written about it without consulting me or giving me any credit. Up until now, most of these authors have got it wrong. The reason is that they do not have any training in scientific disciplines or understand the basic principles of the atomic and quantum structures of the universe. In a way this is understandable as none of us have the capacity to be everything, at least while we are still on Earth, and, in this respect, I would like to have the skills and knowledge of a surgeon but I think my hands are perhaps too shaky these days and I probably do not have enough time left on Earth to obtain the skills, let alone put them into practice.

The Enigma of Life's Vitality

Almost all alternative and complimentary articles in magazines, newspapers and alternative and complementary books make relentless reference to a mystical energy called 'Prana', 'Chi' 'Kie' and so on. Acupuncture is one of the alternative systems of medicine that employs the manipulation of this mystical energy by inserting needles into invisible points of the body called meridians and chakras. The insertion of the needles at these special points is said to change and adjust the flow of the 'chi' energy through invisible channels in the body to re-balance the body's energy towards healing.

More recently in numerous magazine and news papers, a Japanese version of alternative therapy called 'Reiki' has been making the headlines. Many practitioners of these types of alternative practices claim that this mystical energy comes to them from God or some deceased master in heaven. They claim that they are a chosen channel through which God beams this healing power to them through the top of their head and which they can then channel into the patient using their hands. They call this 'hands on' or 'spiritual healing'.

All of these methods have one thing in common and that is that they are unable to explain scientifically what is going on. There is no doubt that patients derive some kind of benefit otherwise the therapies would not have become so popular in the first place. What kind of benefit is gained is always subjective and the type of diseases and symptoms that can be treated is not specified. I will try to make an attempt to explain or at least give a scientific model for what is going on and what this energy is.

The Quantum of Healing

As previously mentioned, surrounding every atom is a cloud of electrons orbiting the nucleus at incredibly high speeds. The speed or frequency of the outer shell (valence) electrons is what determines the colour of matter when white light is shone on it. The speed or frequency of different coloured materials matches a particular frequency of the visible light spectrum and thus being in phase, this then reflects that colour back to the observer. All those frequencies of light that are not reflected back to the observer are absorbed. For example living plants are in the main green, therefore the plant does not absorb this frequency and reflects it back to the universe at large; green is a cold frequency and plants require warm energy to grow, so therefore there is an intelligence in plants that creates chlorophyll to increase their efficiency and it appears to the observer that the plant is green. When the plant dies the frequency of the plant slows down and the leaves turn from yellow to red and then to brown as the energy is dissipated and is not being replaced by the life force. The valence electrons of each atom exchange their orbits and link up with adjacent atoms. These orbit exchanges bond each atom together to form molecules, which are the building blocks of all of the material universe including living cells.

Question: how much energy is required to maintain the very high velocity or speed of an orbiting electron? Electrons, whilst spinning, exhibit the quality of mass and mass in motion consumes energy. But there is a scientific dilemma, the quantum of energy required to maintain the motion is more than is represented by the particle itself. This is an enigma and what is even more mystifying is that every particle radiates energy, which is why they can be detected in the first place. The energy entering an atom cannot be observed to have the equivalent value that it dissipates.

As all particles spin, the problem at the universal level gets out of hand and the universe appears to rapidly consume every unit of available energy in an instant. At absolute zero, minus 273.15 degrees kelvin the universe disappears or collapses back to the void. Where is the energy coming from that maintains the universe? Is it coming from outside of the universe? Even if one could make sense of this enigma, it simply postpones the problem, so it is sensible to stay at the assemblage point or centre of the universe.

In accordance with the law of conservation of energy, perpetual motion cannot exist and yet every particle spins and it spins forever. Particle spin is exempted from this law. Why is this and what is the truth? As already stated the process that is generating the spin is much more fundamental than the mass of the universe itself and this brings us full circle once more - back to the enigma. Where is the energy coming from?

Quite apparently from this observation, one must deduce that mass is a secondary component or characteristic of the universe. Therefore, what is the prime component or fundamental energy behind the universe that creates the spin by which each particle is maintaining its respective motion and differentiates itself from all other particles? What is this elementary exchange of energy that takes place at the most all-embracing level that causes the form of any given particle to reverberate in another place in the universe. What is the energy that creates this sympathetic resonance?

Naturally, alternative therapists will claim that it is 'Chi', 'Prana' or 'Kei' and those persons with spiritual beliefs will tell you that it is God but this brings us full circle once more for it does not scientifically explain what is going on.

Electronic Gem Lamp Therapy uses the dielectric properties of crystalline precious gem stones to induce energy into diseased or injured tissue, organs and glands by sympathetic resonance. The frequency of the energy induced is dictated by the colour of the gem stone used. For example, ruby has a resonant frequency wave length of around 625 nanometres (the frequency of the colour red) and the energy emitted is hot, whereas, emerald has a green frequency of 565 nm and its energy is cold. The gem stones are contained inside a special chamber inside the low voltage lamps and the gems are electronically excited to resonate with low voltage electronic pulses.

The lamps are actually transducers and they are effective for treating serious and life threatening disease without causing the patient any side effects. The light bulb and colour filter are not essential for the transducers to be effective but are included to assist the doctor or nurse to target the precise part of the patient that requires treatment, therefore electronic gem lamp therapy is truly the first versatile non-systemic medicine available today. All of the thousands of patients who have been treated over the years by myself and other practitioners enjoy the therapies, which are extremely pleasant and effective and, so far, no side effects have been observed or reported. For example, simple complaints, such as skin disease, asthma, infections and so on, most often respond with no more than three treatments. The success rate is way above the medical dictionary's placebo phenomena of between 30% and 70% and one can expect results around the 80% level depending on age and the patient's overall health index. Another critical factor is the correct diagnosis of the symptoms and root cause of them, (see below). With youngsters one can expect and achieve results close to 100% often with only a single treatment. Children with asthma respond to this level.

Dielectric resonance will induce energy into materials that are close by or at a distance. At low power levels it can be contained by metal screening which will absorb the energy. Therefore the doctor or nurse who is using the equipment does not receive any long term exposure. The lamps making use of dielectric principles induce energy by exciting the valence electrons of living cells, so the doctor is able to adjust the biological activity (frequency) of sick or injured parts of the patient as he chooses.

Contention over the above scientific facts can be dispelled by reviewing the technical operating principles behind the surgical ruby laser and quartz crystal oscillators mounted in glass vacuum tubes (see *Telecommunications Principles* by R. N. Renton and *Fiberoptic Infrared and Laser Space-Age Projects* by R. E. Iannini). However, it must be pointed out that ruby lasers employ extremely high voltages and power consumption, whereas electronic gem therapy lamps do not employ the same operating principles. By comparison, electronic gem therapy lamps use only around 25 watts of power at 12 volts and are completely safe, this is equivalent to a quarter of the power used in the average domestic light bulb.

Over exposure to the gem lamps will not cause the patient any problem or side effects as the lamps only modulate the frequency of the valence electrons of cells via dielectric resonance. Even if inadvertently the wrong treatment is used, changing to another colour of gem will quickly change the frequency. Injured or sick cells do not have a normal frequency and Electronic Gem Therapy can adjust or modulate their frequency back to a the normal level, thus accelerating the body's healing process. All of this is quite obvious when one thinks about it and I am surprised that no one has discovered it before now.

The Secret Behind the Success

For many years now, I have been struggling to get this book published, indeed I have spent a fortune and thousands of hours attempting to get a British publisher to accept it. Ironically several of the publishers who have turned it down have subsequently published books by other authors that have used photographs and material from this book. Due to this I have deliberately held back a great deal of information waiting for a publisher. Findhorn Press were the first publishers to recognise the universal importance of its contents. This section of the book is a minute portion of what has been deliberately held back until I was absolutely sure that it would be going to press as it is proof that I am the person that has developed both the assemblage point therapies and the electronic therapies. If I had released it sooner, I am sure that it would have found its way into some other author's book or article without reference to me. Having said this, I am always delighted for other writers and researchers to quote from my work, provided that they include my name and references in their work and obtain the permission of the publisher.

One of the keys to my success is the measurement of the biological energy levels of the patient's tissue, organs and glands and then to correct and adjust the energy differentials using electronic gem therapy lamps to target the nerves, tissue, organs or glands which are sick. It is partly due to the following methods that I have been able to provide over many years therapeutic equipment, handbooks, manuals, training and telephone advice to the numerous clinics, doctors and therapists both in the UK and abroad who use our electronic gem therapy lamps for their patients. Without the use of biological energy measurement it would not have been possible to have developed, researched and proved the numerous treatments through to simple and safe methods that anyone can apply. The methods and techniques employed are totally scientific and precision calibrated, further more they are in accordance with orthodox medical

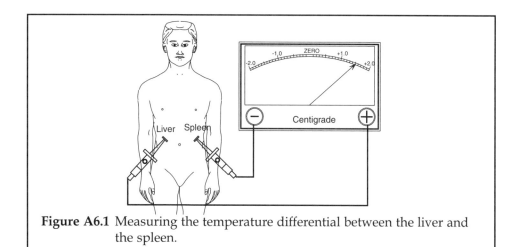

Figure A6.1 Measuring the temperature differential between the liver and the spleen.

scientific knowledge. These methods have provided major breakthroughs in medical treatments which have resulted in unprecedented success rates for the curing of symptoms and disease, including iatrogenic disease which neither alternative or orthodox medicines can currently address.

The following interesting case study is another example that illustrates the value and effectiveness in treating serious disease and also the importance of correct diagnosis. In all chronic skin cases the organ functions must be checked as they are usually responsible With the skin problem represented, the cause of the problem was resolved by treatment to the internal organ malfunctions.

Case Study: Psoriasis or Cirrhosis?

This 60 year old male patient had been diagnosed with psoriasis by his doctor and the hospital and over a period of nine months, despite numerous prescribed medications, the disease had continued to gain ground and was covering perhaps some 30% of his body. The irritation was "driving him insane". He reported that his symptoms had begun shortly after doing some repair work on a farm live stock building. Enjoying beer and cigars, this patient was reluctant to give up either and was in a turmoil of guilt, fear and despair and was concerned that his liver was damaged through drinking beer.

Using differential biological energy sensors calibrated to 0.025 degrees Kelvin, examination revealed that the liver temperature was 1.45 degrees higher than that of his spleen (see Figure A6.1.) Using two lamps, the patient's liver was cooled and calmed with 40 carats of polished emeralds excited with a calming frequency of only 1.5 cycles per second for 20 minutes, by which time the liver temperature had dropped to 0.15 degree negative to the spleen. With this single treatment, his symptoms cleared up in 2 weeks and, a year later, they have not returned despite his continuing to drink beer and smoke cigars.

DISCUSSION: If the liver becomes hot or inflamed, for whatever reason, perhaps it instructs and provides materials for the body to sweat. If the ambient temperature is low, then the skin will not sweat and toxins may build up in the dermis, causing itching and sore patches.

CONCLUSION: Hepatitis (inflammation of the liver) – cause unknown. Giving up smoking and drinking may not have cured his complaint as it may have been an infection or triggered by toxin ingestion.

Generally speaking, these days I only treat patients who have been referred or whom the orthodox medical profession are unable to help. I also treat and research iatrogenic disease, that is, disease caused by previously unsuccessful therapies and medication. Approximately some 25% of hospital beds are now taken up with this disease. However, it is unethical and often difficult to refuse a patient treatment when it is available. In clinical practice the patient's organs are not always measured with electronic equipment as it is much easier and less time consuming to get the nurse to make a physical examination with her hands. However, this requires training and a high degree of sensitivity and experience on the part of the nurse and it does not provide scientific proof as there are no technical data or values to record.

With all of the forgoing discussions it is easy for the scientific and non scientific person to grasp the basic principles of Electronic Gem Lamp Therapy. Colour therapy or phototherapy could not possible achieve these results as it only has a limited penetration on tissue and cannot reach into deep organs. Furthermore, coloured electric light bulbs, even if green, are not cool and do not reduce tissue temperature; they increase skin temperature and dry it out, largely due to the infra-red waves emitted. Coloured electric light bulbs would aggravate most skin conditions and are dangerous since they operate at 240 volts AC, get hot and can cause burns. A greater danger is that the thin glass can and does spontaneously implode, exposing the filament wires, and, if a patient's skin is close to the bulb, it could cause electrocution.

Dangers Caused to the Progress of Science by Misinformation

From a medical ethics perspective and 'The Patient's Charter', in addition to the obvious damage and confusion to both therapists and their patients by authors, therapist and clinics using the terms 'electromagnetic light therapy', 'coloured light therapy' and 'colour therapy' when referring to Electronic Gem Lamp Therapy, there are other factors to be considered. There is now a mounting body of evidence that links electromagnetic radiation to cancer, tumours and miscarriages. Whale Medical's Electronic Gem Lamp Therapy apparatus is expensive, robust and durable medical hardware, assembled under licence by an expert British medical equipment manufacturing company and constructed to meet the tough demands of a busy clinic or hospital. Whale Medical and the manufacturing company have gone to a great amount of effort and substantial expense to manufacture safe therapeutic equipment that complies with British Standards and European Market standards so that it is acceptable to orthodox medicine.

Whale Medical has designed the lamps and other associated hardware so that neither patients nor the therapists are exposed to any electromagnetic radiation. Indeed, the electromagnetic radiation emitted from the lamps is a mere 5 milligauss at a distance of 5.0 centimetres, this compares to a lady's electric razor or cassette tape player which typically has radiation levels of 150 milligauss at 5.0 cm distance. Other common equipment such as TV sets or computer monitors can emit several thousands of milligauss at much greater distances.

Today misinformation is the nemesis of the planet and is the weapon used by covert or veiled hostile people or organisations who attempt and often succeed in intimidating and demoralising enthusiastic and creative individuals into a temperament of appeasement, grief or apathy.

It is the responsibility of every individual to route out complacency and bad ethics and to expose the source of misinformation to the highest authorities. Our survival depends upon the ability of upright scientists and other people of goodwill to break the death grip of the propaganda that is being cultivated and circulated by the hidden forces of the power holders who are controlling and manipulating the health, economic and environmental resources of populations on this planet.

Bibliography

Anon, *The New American Book of the Dead*. Foreword by J. C. Lilly. IDHHB Publishing.

Castaneda, Carlos, Ph.D., *The Teachings of Don Juan: A Yaqui Way of Knowledge*. The University of California Press.

Castaneda, Carlos, Ph.D., *The Fire From Within*. Black Swan.

Castaneda, Carlos, Ph.D., *The Art Of Dreaming*. Harper Collins.

Castaneda, Carlos, Ph.D., *Magical Passes*. Thorsons.

The Daily Mail, 6 December 1999, page 5, column 1.

Duesberg, Peter, Ph.D. & Yiamuyiamnis, J., Ph.D., *A.I.D.S.: H.I.V. Doesn't Cause A.I.D.S., Recreational and Medical Drugs Do*. Health Action Press.

Evens-Wentz, W.Y., *The Tibetan Book of The Dead*. Oxford University Press.

Hobday, Richard, MSc, Phd. *The Healing Sun, Sunlight and Health in the 21st Century*. Findhorn Press.

Hoffman, A. Evans Shultes, *The Plants of the Gods*. Hutchinsons.

Iannini. Robert E. *Fiberoptic, Infrared and Laser Space Age Projects*. Tab Books Inc. 1987

Krishna, Gopi, *The Awakening of Kundalini*. E. P. Dutton & Company..

Lancot, Guylaine, M.D., *The Medical Mafia*. Here's The Key Inc..

Landymore-Lim, Dr. L., *Poisonous Prescriptions*. PODD.

Leary, Dr. Timothy, *The Politics of Ecstasy*. Paladin.

Leary, Dr. Timothy, Metzner, Ralph and Alpert, Richard, *The Psychedelic Experience*. Academy Editions.

Lilly, Dr. John C., *The Centre Of The Cyclone*. Calder & Boyars Ltd..

Lilly, Dr. John C., *The Deep Self. Profound Relaxation and the Tank Isolation Technique*. Simon and Schuster.

Moss, R.W., Ph.D., *Questioning Chemotherapy*. Equinox Books.

Renton. R.N., *Telecommunications Principles*. Pitman 1950

Scot-Mumby, Keith., MB, ChB. *Virtual Medicine*. Thorsons.

Stortebecker, Patrick, M.D., Ph.D., *Dental Caries as a Cause of Nervous Disorders*. Bio-Probe Inc..

Trull, Louise B,. *The Cancell Controversy, Why is a possible cure for cancer being suppressed?* Hampton Roads.

Walker, Martin J., *Dirty Medicine*. Slingshot Publications.

Weatherall, D.J., Leddingham, J.G.G. and Warrell D.A., *The Oxford Textbook of Medicine*. Oxford University Press.

Wilson, Robert Anton, *Prometheus Rising*. Falcon Press.

Index

Q

Quack	69
quartz	183, 185
crystal	97, 98, 99, 113, 125, 183, 185
crystal oscillators	217
quicksilver	69

R

radiation therapy	5, 61, 159
radio	
transmission stations	11
waves	11
record form	177
red	128, 153, 194, 195, 205, 206, 215, 216
coral	128
reflex times	96
rehabilitation	49, 60, 64
Reiki	34, 214
reincarnation	39, 78
relaxation	37, 109, 138
religion	30
religious cult brainwashing	72
Renton, R. N.	217
resin	64
respiration	58, 67, 178, 180
rheumatism	3, 123, 124, 154, 211
rhinitis	126
root canals	68
rose water	122, 123
ruby	20, 109, 116, 117, 119, 120, 125, 126, 128, 129, 134, 151, 153, 156, 159, 195, 204, 205, 206, 217

S

S.T.P.	65
sanity	73
sapphire	53, 111, 119, 127, 128, 129, 136, 137, 138, 139, 140, 141, 142, 143, 144, 150, 151, 152, 153, 156, 157, 159, 163, 190
blue	53, 109, 111, 123, 127, 128, 134, 135, 136, 137, 138, 143, 144, 145, 148, 154, 155, 191, 195, 208
yellow	127, 128, 143, 146, 147, 149, 153, 155, 195
scalds	153
scanning	210
scans	198
scar tissue formation	155
schizophrenia	3, 18, 27, 36, 47, 59, 87, 105
states	46
schizophrenics	47
sciatica	5, 124, 136, 155, 163, 187, 191
scleroderma	140
security	44
sedative	123
seizures	59
self control	77
self hypnosis	34
semen	122
semiconductor solar panels	12
senile dementia	3, 18, 30, 146, 157, 158
sensuality	27
sexual	
constraint	34, 72
deviations	27
energy	35
hormones	45
libido	147
shaman	97
Shaman's Blow, the	96
shell shock	50
shift	171
in depth	171, 172
shingles	127
shock	17, 157, 191
shoulder pain	187
side effects	8, 198, 217
seizures	
grand mal	59
petty mal	59
silicon dioxide	113
silver	11, 12, 121
amalgam	68
singing	96, 172, 173
sinus	146
problems	21, 52, 146
skeletal problems	153
skin	53, 85, 86, 87, 121, 143, 145, 204, 206, 208, 219, 220
burn	148, 152, 153

U

V

W

FINDHORN
Press

Findhorn Press is the publishing business of the Findhorn Community which has grown around the Findhorn Foundation in northern Scotland.

For further information about the Findhorn Foundation and the Findhorn Community, please contact:

Findhorn Foundation
The Visitors Centre
The Park, Findhorn IV36 3TY, Scotland, UK
tel 01309 690311• fax 01309 691301
email reception@findhorn.org
www.findhorn.org

For a complete Findhorn Press catalogue, please contact:

Findhorn Press

The Park, Findhorn,   P. O. Box 13939
Forres IV36 3TY   Tallahassee
Scotland, UK   Florida 32317-3939, USA
Tel 01309 690582   Tel (850) 893 2920
freephone 0800-389-9395   toll-free 1-877-390-4425
Fax 01309 690036   Fax (850) 893 3442
e-mail info@findhornpress.com
www.findhornpress.com

Medicine Hands: Massage Therapy for People with Cancer
by Gayle MacDonald, M.S., L.M.T,

"...an excellent resource which has long been needed by health professionals. It is full of wise advice for both patients and therapists. From my personal experience as a patient and as a physician, it speaks the truth."
—Dr. Bernie Siegel, author of *Prescriptions for Living*

"...a welcome resource for individuals living with cancer and for all caregivers"
—Dawn Nelson, author of *Compassionate Touch*

"...a unique, comprehensive guide to the use of massage in helping cancer patients to heal. I highly recommend it for practitioners, patients and caregivers alike".
—Joe Coletto, National College of Naturopathic Medicine

Medicine Hands debunks a pervasive health myth that massage is anathema for those suffering with cancer. The idea that cancer can metastasize as a result of massage is not rooted in any science. This book cites clinical evidence that proves just the opposite. Touch and massage are vital to a cancer patient's health and well-being.

  Medicine Hands is a practical book written for both health professionals and the lay person. Research is highlighted with anecdotes, stories, and vignettes of cancer patients, massage therapists, caregivers, hospice workers and other health professionals. Practical information is presented on administering touch, drug-related considerations, providing care at home, and dealing with hospital and hospice situations.

  Medicine Hands is an invaluable resource for:
  • Massage therapists and other touch therapists
  • Cancer patients and their caregivers and families
  • Oncologists and cancer treatment centers
  • Natural health clinics
  • Massage and other alternative medicine schools and educational settings
  • Health care professionals — nurses, doctors, hospice workers — who come into contact with cancer patients

Gayle MacDonald, M.S., L.M.T, a long time health educator and veteran massage therapist, finds that her personal and professional interests are inseparable. It was after suffering ill health herself that she became the health and physical educator she had always wanted to be. She continues to teach in her native Oregon, helping others to expand their awareness that in massage they are performing a service that integrates the sacred with the mundane, and that they not only touch their patients body, but also their heart, mind and soul.

ISBN 1-899171-77-0 Findhorn Press Paperback

The Healing Sun: Sunlight and Health in the 21st Century
by Richard Hobday, M Sc, PhD

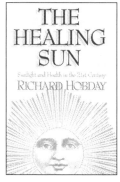

"No factual work that I have read in the last ten years has held my attention for so long as The Healing Sun... If you only read one book this century, do yourself a favour and make it this one!"
—Keith Hall, Editor, *Building for a Future*

"Here is an important book whose message we ignore at our peril."
—Sandra Goodman, PhD , Editor, *Positive Health*

"This is a very well written book, full of interesting information for the lay reader and clearly very carefully researched. Dr Hobday does not shrink from controversy, nor from stamping on what he perceives to be feet of clay. Thoroughly recommended for the increasing body of people who are seeking alternative methods of natural healing."
—Professor C. J. McVeigh, Editor, *Ambient Energy*

The human race evolved under the sun, and for thousands of years lived in harmony with its heat and light. Yet over the last fifty years we have lost this close contact with the sun and its healing powers. We have become afraid of it.

Yet the sun is central to our well being and health. Did you know that:
- sunlight can help prevent and heal many common and often fatal diseases like breast cancer, heart disease, multiple sclerosis and osteoporosis
- prolonged exposure to artificial light puts the body under great stress
- large numbers of people may be compromising their health through sunlight deficiency
- there is a substantial body of historical and contemporary evidence that suggests moderate sunbathing is far more beneficial than we are currently led to believe

The light and heat from the sun are indispensable to all nature. Humanity is also part of nature and needs sunlight for health and well being, for vitality and happiness. This book explains how and why we should welcome sunlight back into our lives — safely! It shows how sunlight was used to prevent and cure diseases in the past, and how it can heal us and help us in the future.

Richard Hobday, MSc, PhD is a member of the British Register of Complementary Practitioners and has studied traditional Chinese Medicine and Chinese exercise systems in China. Dr. Hobday has many years experience of solar design in buildings and is a leading authority on the history of sunlight therapy.

ISBN 1-899171-97-5   Findhorn Press Paperback